Growing-Up Stories for Four's and Five's

GROWING-UP STORIES
FOR FOUR'S

AND FIVE'S

Bible teaching
for
everyday living

*Correlated with the
Beginner All-Bible Sunday
School lessons and Church-
time for Four's and Five's,
but equally suitable for use
in any children's meetings
or for reading at home.*

Compiled by Mary E. LeBar

Published by
SCRIPTURE PRESS FOUNDATION
1825 College Avenue, Wheaton, Illinois

Contents

	PAGE		PAGE
A verse learned twice	45	Missionary picnic	49
Amy's search	55	Moving day	96
Besides that!	17	Nancy the nurse	93
Big enough	104	Neighbors	52
Billy and the queer little man	8	One shiny coin	18
Billy and the snow children	57	Petey's party	62
Billy's biggest smile	27	Philip and The Finisher	75
Blow wind, blow!	70	Ready for Christmas	64
Chuckie learns	97	Sandra decides	41
Connie's promise	42	Second pair of hands	50
Debby's promise	66	Stephen's problem	9
Dickie, Ahgupuk, and Jola	6	Steps	103
Dorie's gray day	54	Strong gentle hands	99
Double helpers	47	Surprise by airmail	46
Edwin's share	90	The beautiful pink cake	23
Elizabeth Jones	31	The Best Builder	53
Empty pockets	10	The big slide	29
First day at school	44	The big something	74
Follow the leader	79	The busy day	28
Friends of Jesus	73	The castle game	25
Friendship station	5	The echo	85
Georgie's uncle's wheelchair	51	The empty bottle	98
Gordon's answer	87	The exchange	56
Gumdrops for Harry	40	The four pennies	95
Handy Andy	83	The girl who found a Helper	16
Happy day	82	The glad Gays	2
Hidden power	58	The high-up doorbell	38
How Hilty helped	36	The kind uncle	72
How it happened	101	The lily	81
In the garden	80	The little country church	24
In the hospital	15	The little house	102
In the toy shop	91	The little pine tree	13
It was Martha!	34	The little red wagon	39
Judy's shoe	33	The little teachers who learned	
Karen	77	a lesson	7
Leslie's plan	60	The littlest cousin	100
Lisbeth and Louise	88	The missing gift	11
Little eyes, little ears	76	The new neighbors	19
Little ones, too	65	The noisy tick-tock clock	20
Lora's friend	78	The red coat	1
Lost and found Judy	32	The shoe bank	61
Me too!	30	The silver pitcher	4

	PAGE		PAGE
The sled	71	The very little voice	26
The spot	94	The wonderful seeds	3
The stolen trike	92	Three lost nickels	21
The story lady	84	Timmy's adventure	67
The thumpy sounds	37	Tony gets even	48
The train station	14	Two pennies for Nancy	43
The travels of a penny	59	Virginia's loving gift	63
The two bells	12	What Jean found	68
The two Ellens	69	Whistling boy	86
The two wishes	89	Who will? I will!	35
The very best Book	22		

Preface

"Tell me a story!"

Do your four- and five-year-olds plead for stories until you literally "run out" of good ones? Do you wish you had suitable stories—stories which interest and guide little children, which would help to bring them up in the nurture and admonition of the Lord? If so, you'll be reaching for this book daily—at home and in church.

These stories have been especially compiled for use with the course, *Church-time for Four's and Five's*. Each story has been prepared following the same aim and based on the same Bible verse as the Bible story taught in the Sunday School hour. The purpose of these conduct stories is to make practical the truth of each Bible story.

Since Beginner-age children have such a limited experience and vocabulary, stories which hold their interest, as well as meet their needs, are hard to find. But here are 104 made-to-order stories! The writers of these stories have given you appealing, life-related stories with a heart-reaching Christian message.

Christian workers will find innumerable ways to utilize these modern-day incidents in all kind of children's meetings. Parents, too, will treasure this collection of 104 stories as an enjoyable way to convey to their children what is acceptable Christian conduct. Four's and five's will enjoy the same stories at home that they hear in Beginner Church. In fact—they'll demand them! Incidentally, you adults will enjoy these stories and profit by them too.

The red coat

"Grandmother," Alice said, tugging at her coat, "I can't button it!"

Grandmother didn't answer. She was dressing small Peter and making a clucking sound, the way she did whenever something bothered her.

"You really must have a new coat, Peter," Granny said.

Then she tried to button the blue coat Alice had worn for two winters and she made the clucking sound again.

Alice laughed. "I guess I'll have to get a new coat, too," she said. Then she saw the worry line in Granny's forehead and wondered what was wrong.

"I could move the buttons over," Granny said. "But that's the best we can do with *your* coat, Alice."

"Well, if Peter gets a new coat, why can't I have one?" Alice asked.

"Because there isn't enough money. And until Grandfather gets home . . ." Granny shook her head. "We can buy a coat for you *or* one for Peter."

Alice looked at Peter and thought how much she loved him. She wished Granny didn't have to wear that worry line in her forehead.

"I don't mind my old coat," she said. "Let Peter have a new one."

Granny hugged her and Peter gave her a sunny smile.

"I *feel* beautiful," she said. "Kind of all dressed up in love!"

So Alice went to Sunday School feeling all dressed up in love. But her best friend, Erma, came all dressed up in a lovely new red coat!

When they got home Alice said, eagerly, "Erma has a new red coat. I do wish I could have one just like it!"

The worry line came back in Granny's forehead.

"Oh, Granny!" Alice clapped her hand over her mouth. "I didn't mean to tell you . . . It just came out!"

Alice was careful not to mention the coat again. And when Peter got his new coat she just pulled her sleeves down as far as she could, so Granny wouldn't see how very short they were.

Small Peter felt sorry for Alice. But Alice told him, "God cares for us and when *He* thinks I need a coat—I 'spect He'll see that I get one."

At last Grandfather came home from the far city where his business had sent him. He had an armful of gifts. There was a shiny black engine for Peter, a book for Granny. Alice's box was big and flat. She tore the paper away.

"Oh, Grandfather!" she cried. *"How did you know?"*

Granny said, "The weather was warm when you left, so how *did* you know that she had outgrown her old winter coat?"

"I didn't," Grandfather admitted. "I just saw this coat in a window and I thought of Alice."

Alice tried on the new red coat. "Thank you, *thank you,* Grandfather!" Then she whispered in his ear, *"I think God must have told you to get it."*

— —AILEENE SARGENT

"He cares for you"
—I Peter 5:7.

1

The glad Gays

Everyone said that the Gay family was the happiest family in town. Perhaps that was because there were so many Gay children. There was Andy, who was the oldest, then the five-year-old twins, Ted and Peg. Jill came next, then little Tina. People passing the house could hear girl voices and boy voices, play sounds and gay sounds all day long.

But one day Father Gay came home from work in the middle of the day and Mother Gay looked very solemn.

"Grandmother is sick," she explained. "Father and I must go to her at once. We can't get back tonight but Mrs. Worth will take care of you."

"You must be good children," Father said. "Promise?"

"Sure," said Andy and the twins.

"Sure," said Jill.

"Sure," piped little Tina.

At dinner it seemed very strange to see Mrs. Worth sitting in Mother's place. She was kind as could be and the food was good. But Peg said she wasn't hungry and Ted pushed his plate away, saying, "I don't like that."

"Mother always cuts mine for me," Jill complained.

Little Tina began to whimper. Then she cried loud and long.

Poor Mrs. Worth didn't know what to do. It was even worse at night, for the children didn't like having strange hands help them get ready for bed. And they missed the Bible story Father always read at sleepy-time.

Anyone passing the Gay home that afternoon or evening must surely have thought that the Gays had moved away. For there were no play sounds or gay sounds loud enough to be heard. It was a sad kind of quiet.

Andy didn't go to sleep for a long time. He had to think about something.

Since children, like birds, wake up before grownups do, Andy gathered his brother and sisters around him long before Mrs. Worth began moving about in the kitchen. "Listen!" he whispered. "We felt bad yesterday because Mother and Father are away. Why, not having them here is like—like—"

"Like a big emptiness," Peg said.

"Yes," said Andy. "But what if we didn't have *anyone* to take care of us?"

A little later they tiptoed down the stairs to the kitchen door. When Mrs. Worth turned around they sang out, "Good morning, Mrs. Worth."

And Mrs. Worth knew that the Gay children were no longer sad.

While they were eating breakfast the phone rang and they heard her say, "Oh, yes, Mr. Gay. They're very good children today. Andy wants to talk to you."

"Hello, Father," Andy said into the telephone. "We weren't good yesterday but we're sorry now. And Father—we told God this morning we're sure glad He gave us you and Mother—and Mrs. Worth, too!"

— —AILEENE SARGENT

"He cares for you"

—I Peter 5:7.

2

The wonderful seeds

Nancy and Joan stood outside the grocery store where Mother was shopping and watched the big truck drive up and stop. It was loaded with crates of oranges and lettuce, boxes of apples, and huge bags of potatoes.

"Where did the man in the truck get them?" Nancy wanted to know.

The girls went into the store to ask Mother. They saw so many things, that by the time they found her, they had forgotten what they wanted to ask.

When Mother finished, they all went home. And what a pleasant surprise! Grandfather was there.

He hugged Nancy and Joan. "I wonder if you two girls would like to come to the farm for a few days."

"*I* would, Grandfather," Nancy cried.

"*Please* take us," Joan begged.

And so, after a while, Grandfather, Nancy, and Joan drove off to the farm.

Nancy chattered about the fun they would have in the swing. Joan was eager to see how big the baby chicks had grown. But Grandfather talked about vegetables that had grown from seeds the girls had helped him plant weeks before.

"Grandfather likes to *tease*," Nancy whispered to Joan.

"He *pretends* sometimes, too," Joan whispered to Nancy.

They were sure he had just been *pretending* when they had helped him plant the seeds. So they had played his game and pretended vegetables would come out of the ground. Didn't everybody know that you buy vegetables in a store?

They arrived at the farm and were greeted by Grandmother, who gave them cookies and milk.

"Now then," said Grandfather. "Let's go see our vegetables."

Nancy and Joan followed, giggling. As if vegetables could come out of tiny seeds not much bigger than grains of sand!

But outside the kitchen door they stood still and stared. There were a row of bushes with long green beans hanging from the branches, and vines with red tomatoes hanging heavily down. Grandfather showed them how to grasp a fern-like plant and pull a golden carrot right out of the earth.

"Did these really come from the seeds we put here?" Nancy asked.

"Really!" said Grandfather.

Grandfather wasn't pretending. His eyes and voice were full of awe. "Wondeful!" he said, looking at the garden.

"Wonderful, *wonderful!*" Nancy echoed.

But Joan looked up at the blue sky. "Nobody but *God* could do it," she said.

"Wonderful, *wonderful*, WONDERFUL GOD!"

————Aileene Sargent

"He cares for you"
—I Peter 5:7.

3

The silver pitcher

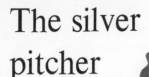

It stood on a shelf in the dining room — the silver pitcher that was very old and (for some reason Linda could not understand) very precious. Once a stranger offered a lot of money for it. But Mother wouldn't sell it.

"It's so old," Linda said. "Why did the man want to pay so much for it?"

"Because it is beautiful," Mother said, "and there is no other pitcher quite like it."

"Then we must be rich to have it," Linda said.

Father looked up from his newspaper with a twinkle in his eye. "We'll never be poor," he said, "as long as we have Mother's silver pitcher."

Now Father was joking but Linda did not know that. And so she thought that as long as they kept the silver pitcher, they would have all they needed.

Then one day the shelf where the silver pitcher stood was bare!

"Mother!" Linda cried. "Where is the silver pitcher?"

"I gave it to Aunt Mary this afternoon," Mother said, calmly.

"He cares for you"
—I Peter 5:7.

"Without the silver pitcher," Linda cried, "we'll be *poor*—maybe *hungry!*"

Father stared. "Linda!" he said. "Don't you know who cares for us?"

But Linda ran off and would not listen.

The next morning she sat down to eat her breakfast. She looked at the shelf where the silver pitcher used to stand. An open Bible lay there.

While she was wondering about it Father took it down and began to read.

"What are you reading about, Father?" Linda asked, eagerly.

"About our heavenly Father's promise to take care of us," he said. "Here Jesus tells us to think about the flowers that grow in gardens and fields. Do you know, Linda, that the richest king in all the world could not buy clothing half so beautiful as the dresses the flowers wear?"

"That's because God dresses the flowers," Linda said.

"And the birds," Father went on. "They don't store up food in barns. But day by day they find enough to eat."

"That's because God takes care of the birds," Linda said.

Father frowned thoughtfully. "Now I wonder," he said, "why should God's *children* need a silver pitcher?"

Linda laughed joyously. "Oh, Father, we don't!" she cried. "God will give us everything we need—*if we trust Him*. The silver pitcher—well, I know now that the silver pitcher was just something pretty. That's all. Just—something—pretty."

— —AILEENE SARGENT

4

Friendship station

David tied his wagon to the back of Barry's tricycle and Barry tied his tricycle to the back of Joe's auto. It made a splendid train. But each time they rode past the new house, David looked at the window and forgot to help push the train with his foot.

Joe looked back. "Hey!" he said, scowling. "You going to play train?"

"That lady," David said, "sits there in the window all the time."

"So what?" Joe asked rudely.

"So maybe she's lonely," David said.

"*All abo-oard!*" Barry called loudly.

Joe began to pedal as fast as he could and the other boys did their part to help the train move swiftly along.

But the next time they passed the new house David dragged his foot on the ground to stop the train.

Joe and Barry looked around.

"That lady wiggled her finger at me," David said. "I think she wants me."

Joe didn't care. Especially when *he* was the engineer.

"*I* wouldn't go," Barry said. "Anyway, you don't even know her."

"She looks sad," David said. "Maybe if I just say hello, she will smile."

"He cares for you"
—1 Peter 5:7.

"Aw, forget about her," Joe said. "Let's go. *All abo-o-oard!*"

David jumped off.

"You—you *can't* forget other people," he said. "God never forgets *us.*"

David ran up the walk. The door stood ajar, for it was a warm day. He reached up to ring the bell and heard the soft BING-BONG sound in the house. Then a voice called, "Come in."

Slowly he pushed the door open and walked into the room where the lady sat.

"Hello," he said. "I'm David."

Then suddenly he felt shy and could not say another word. The lady was in a wheel chair! That meant she couldn't walk!

"Why, hello—David," she said. And her voice was as friendly as her face. "How nice of you to come to visit me. Do you know—I have been sitting here for the longest time, unable to move this wheel chair because my sweater slipped over the side and got tangled in the wheel. Could you help me?"

David was glad to have something to do. After a time he managed to get the sleeve of the sweater from between the spokes of the wheel. He lifted it to her lap.

When he came out of her house he was munching a large sugar cooky. The train slowed and stopped. Joe and Barry looked enviously at the cooky.

"Who gave you that?" Joe asked.

David opened his mouth to answer—but he didn't know the lady's name! Then he smiled happily. "My *friend,*" he said. "My friend in there."

———AILEENE SARGENT

5

Dickie, Ahgupuk, and Jola

Dickie had a new home. While it was being built he often went with his father to watch the men saw the boards and lay the bricks that made such fine walls.

"Where did we get the brick and wood?" Dickie asked his father.

"Come," said his father. "I will show you."

He took Dickie to the forest to see the tall trees that would be cut down and sawed into boards. Then they went to a factory where men make bricks of clay.

"God gives us what we need for shelter," Father said.

"Trees and clay!" Dickie said, wonderingly. "God put them here for us to use."

 Ahgupuk is an Eskimo boy who lives in a cold country covered with snow and ice all year. But Ahgupuk has a snug home too. It is an igloo.

One day he asked his father, "What is our igloo made of?"

"From blocks of ice and the skin of seals," his father answered. "Come. I will show you."

They sat on a sled, pulled by two Husky dogs. The dogs ran swiftly over the ice to a place where some men were building an igloo. Ahgupuk watched the men cut the blocks of ice and set them side by side in a circle, then row upon row, until the igloo rose up like an enormous hollow snowball. Then he saw the seals swimming in the icy sea. Their skins would be used to line the igloo and make it warm.

"God provides what we need for shelter," the father said.

Ahgupuk nodded. "Everything we need is here. All we have to do is *use* it."

Jola is a dark - skinned boy who lives in a very warm country, where it never snows.

"What is our hut made of, Father?" Jola asked.

"Come," said his father. "I will show you." And he took Jola to see a new hut their neighbors were building.

Long slender poles were driven into the ground in a circle and the tops of the poles were pulled together. Then the people cut grass—grass that grew taller than Jola—to weave in and out between the poles.

"You see," Jola's father said, "God gives us what we need for shelter."

"Yes," said Jola. "All we have to do is to make good use of His gifts."

— —Aileene Sargent

"He cares for you"
—I Peter 5:7.

6

The little teachers who learned a lesson

Barbara came into the kitchen carrying her doll and a tiny pair of shoes.

"Mother," she said, "my dolly has *two* pair of shoes, but Sue's dolly hasn't any. Would it be all right if I gave Sue my dolly's extra pair?"

"I think that would be very nice," Mother said.

"And I'm going to give Sue and Ronnie some of my peanuts," said Carl.

In a little while, Carl and Barbara came back home in a huff.

"What's the matter?" Mother asked. "Didn't Sue like the doll shoes?"

"Oh, yes," Barbara said, in a cross voice. "She liked them all right! But she didn't even thank me for them!"

"They ate most all of my peanuts," Carl burst out, "but they never said *thank you!* Not even once!"

"So we aren't going to play with them any more," Barbara said.

"Well, that's too bad," Mother said. "Because you could be an example."

Barbara was thoughtful. "You mean, if Carl and I always remember to say *thank you*, maybe they'll learn?"

Mother nodded.

Next day Sue and Ronnie's mother invited Barbara and Carl to lunch. When they came home, Mother asked, "Did you enjoy your visit?"

"Oh, yes," Barbara said. "But we made an *awful* mistake, Mother!"

"What happened?" Mother asked. "Did you forget your manners?"

"No, *ma'am*," Carl said. "Why, I said *thank you* so often, pretty soon Sue and Ronnie began saying it. And that's mostly all we said at lunch. But—" He looked at the floor. "*You* tell, Barbie."

"Well," Barbie said, "Mrs. Baxter put the food on our plates and we kept saying, 'Thank you, Mrs. Baxter.' And when everyone was served, we began to eat, and then . . ."

"And then?" Mother urged.

Barbara hung her head. "Then everybody was so quiet, I looked up. And there was Mrs. Baxter, and Sue and Ronnie, with their heads bowed. And then," Barbara finished slowly, "Mrs. Baxter *thanked God* for giving us the food."

Now Mother was looking at the floor. "I'm afraid," she said, sadly, "that we have been very thoughtless in our home. We remember to thank others for their kindness but we *forget to thank God for all His goodness to us!*"

"Well," Barbie said, with a big sigh, "we thought we could teach Sue and Ronnie about good manners but *we* learned something more important from them."

— —AILEENE SARGENT

"I will give Thee thanks with my whole heart" —Psalm 138:1, A.S.V.

Billy and the queer little man

"What a *fine* boy!" said the new neighbor, smiling at Billy.

But Billy's mother didn't say anything. She knew he quarreled with his friends and shouted, "I wish I could go where there aren't any other children!"

He wished it would never rain and didn't care if the trees *were* thirsty. He tired of his toys, grumbled about his food, and hated to wear his coat.

"What an *ungrateful* boy!" Father said, when he tucked Billy into bed.

All at once, Billy didn't know how he got there, but he found himself in a strange place, where there was neither trees nor grass. A queer little man sat on the side of a hill, eating something.

"I'm hungry," Billy told him.

The queer little man broke a chunk off the hill and handed it to Billy.

"Ugh!" said Billy, when he'd tasted it. "I want some *food!*"

"That's too bad," the little man said. "But you don't like food."

Billy looked about. "Aren't there any other children here?" he asked.

"You don't like other children," the little man reminded Billy.

"Well, when you brought me here,"

"I will give Thee thanks with my whole heart" —Psalm 138:1, A.S.V.

Billy said, "didn't you bring my toys?"

The little man shook his head. "You don't like your toys," he said.

Billy sighed. He wondered what to do. He felt cold and wished he had his coat. The little man guessed what he was thinking and spoke sharply.

"You don't like to wear a coat!"

It was getting colder all the time— and darker, too. Billy thought of his warm comfortable home and wished he could find it. And he wished—oh, how he wished for his father and mother!

"I want to go home!" he sobbed. "I want my mother and father!"

He thought of all the wonderful things God had given him and how ungrateful he had been. Just then something soft touched his cheek. It must be a leaf! Was there a tree in this gray land? He reached out his arms and . . . .

There was Mother bending over him.

"Oh, Mother," he cried, hugging her. "I had a horrible dream about a queer little man and—Mother! I think I'll say 'thank You' to God right now for all the good things He has given me!"

And after that Billy didn't forget to thank God for his home, his parents, his food and friends, and yes—even for rain on thirsty ground!

"What a fine boy!" said the new neighbor, the next time she met Billy and his mother.

"Yes," said Billy's mother. "He *is* a fine boy." You see, she knew that Billy had changed. Instead of always *wanting* things to be different, now he was thankful for what he had.

— —AILEENE SARGENT

Stephen's problem

The stories Stephen liked best were those about Jesus, especially the *gift* stories. One was about the wise men, who brought gifts to the Baby Jesus. And one was about a boy who gave Jesus his lunch. Then there was the woman who gave Jesus her precious perfume. Stephen wished that he, too, could give a gift to Jesus.

He looked at his toys and shook his head. Then he talked to his playmates.

"We're just children," they said, as if Jesus wouldn't expect anything from children.

Around the corner Stephen had many friends. There was the carpenter, Mr. Peters; and Joe, who repaired shoes; and Dr. Martin, who had helped Stephen the time his tooth ached.

He pushed open the door of Joe's shop.

"Well, Stephen," Joe said, "you look troubled this morning."

"I want to give a gift to Jesus," Stephen said. "But I haven't anything."

Joe glanced at Stephen's feet and said, "Ah, yes you have, Stephen. You have a pair of willing feet. Every time you run an errand for your mother I'm sure Jesus is pleased."

Stephen was doubtful. In a few minutes he said "Good-by" and left.

When he peeked into Dr. Martin's office, the dentist said, "Another toothache, Stephen?"

"No, Sir," Stephen replied. "It's just something I want to know. What can a child give Jesus?"

The doctor thought for a moment. Then he said, "I know! Your lips and your tongue. You just say a cheery word when someone is sad and see that your tongue speaks nothing bad."

Stephen sighed. Surely a *gift* must be something you could hold in your hands!

So he went to see the carpenter.

"Mr. Peters," he said, "I would like to give a gift to Jesus. Can you think of *anything* I could give?"

Mr. Peters laid down his hammer and smiled. "Yes," he said. "You just give a helping hand to anyone who needs it and I think Jesus will count that the same as a gift to Him."

Stephen felt confused. He went home thinking of his friends' advice.

"Mother," he asked, "what could I give to Jesus?"

"What do you *want* to give, Stephen?" Mother asked.

Stephen wondered. . . . His hands? His feet? His lips?

Suddenly he looked up with a happy smile. "I know now!" he said. "I want to give Him *all* of me."

Mother nodded. *"That's* the kind of gift Jesus likes best of all," she said.

———AILEENE SARGENT

"Freely you have received, freely give"
—Matthew 10:8.

Empty pockets

"Tony! Roger! Jane!'' Father called.

The three children came running and saw that Father held three large coins in his hand.

"Do you know," he asked them, "how Mother and I divide the money I earn each week?"

"Yes," said Jane. "You put some in an envelope for church."

Tony nodded. "You put some in an envelope for food, too," he said.

"You save some," Roger added.

"That's right," Father said. "But all week you children beg for candy and ice cream. I don't know *what* you spend."

The children looked at one another. Weren't they going to be allowed any more candy and ice cream?

"So," Father went on, "I am going to give each of you a half dollar every Monday morning. That will buy plenty of candy and ice cream. But save some for your Sunday School offering."

The children felt rich indeed! Tony licked his lips as he thought of all the candy and ice cream he could buy. Roger dropped his whole half dollar into his bank. Jane was thoughtful.

"Father," she said. "Could you give me little pieces of money instead?"

So Father gave Jane five dimes. She put two of them in the pocket of her best coat. They were for Sunday school. Two she put in her purse to spend. The last one she dropped into her bank.

"I'd like little pieces of money, too," Tony said. "A *lot* of them."

Father took Tony's half dollar and gave him a lot of nickels and pennies.

Tony jingled them in his pocket and every time he went to the store with Mother he bought candy or a cone.

Roger wanted Tony and Jane to share their money with him. "I'm saving mine," Roger said.

"You're stingy," Tony told him.

"*You* won't have anything left for Sunday School," Jane said to Tony.

Tony jingled the money in his pocket. He was sure there would be plenty *left over* for the offering.

But when Sunday came Tony's pockets were empty!

Roger went to his bank and shook it hard. Only one penny came out. He had already shaken out the money he had saved for a pair of ice skates.

When the offering box was passed in Sunday School, Jane dropped two dimes in the box. Roger blushed as he dropped in his penny. Poor Tony hung his head; he had nothing to give.

The next day Father again gave each of them a half dollar.

"If we buy everything we want *first*," Tony said, "and just give to the Lord what we have *left over* . . . ."

"Why," Roger broke in, "maybe we won't have any church at all!"

The next Sunday you may be sure Tony and Roger had their offering ready.

——Aileene Sargent

"Freely you have received, freely give" —Matthew 10:8.

The missing gift

Trudy could hardly wait for Christmas to come. They were going to Aunt Martha's. Trudy was so eager to go that Uncle Henry came to get her two whole weeks before Christmas. She found her cousins, Betty and Drew, busy doing anything they could to earn money. "To buy our gifts," they explained.

"Will I have to earn money to buy my own presents?" Trudy asked.

"You should," said Drew.

Trudy didn't think much of the idea but if that was the way they did things here at Aunt Martha's, she guessed she would have to earn some money, too. She knew just what she wanted to buy, but since Betty and Drew had so many secrets she decided she wouldn't tell.

A Christmas tree was set up in the living room and the house was filled with laughter and excitement. But *something* seemed to be missing.

Trudy worked hard to earn money for her gifts. Finally shopping day came. Drew took the two little girls into town. Trudy tried to be patient while the others bought handkerchiefs and pot holders and such things.

"It's your turn, Trudy," they said. "You haven't bought any gifts yet."

"What I want is right near the door," said Trudy. "Now turn your backs."

Later, at home, Drew wrote names on little tags for Trudy and she wrapped each gift in tissue paper.

Early Christmas morning she slipped out of bed and took her gifts to the living room. Heaps of packages lay beneath the tree. Trudy placed hers in a little pile apart from the others.

After breakfast the gifts were opened, Trudy's last of all.

"What's this?" Uncle Henry asked.

"It's a shepherd," Trudy told him.

"I have one too!" said Aunt Martha.

Betty had the third shepherd and Drew got the stable. Father held a tiny figure of Joseph, while Mother smiled tenderly at her little blue-robed Mary.

The stable was set up and Drew stood the little figures in place. Uncle Henry read the tag on the last gift, "FOR EVERYBODY." Then he said, "You open this one, Trudy."

Trudy removed the wrappings from the last gift—the manger in which lay a wee Babe. She set it carefully in front of Mary.

Everyone was very quiet. Trudy was so happy she could hardly breathe. *This* was what had been missing. She looked around.

"Christmas is for loving and not just laughing," she said. *"You can't have Christmas without thinking about the Lord Jesus."*

— —AILEENE SARGENT

"He loved us, and sent His Son"
—I John 4:10.

The two bells

One day the bell factory finished making two bells—Mr. Red Bell and Mr. Silver Bell. They were both ready to be sold.

Mr. Red Bell said to himself, "I hope a church buys me. I want to call people to worship God. I want to ring out, 'Ding! Dong! Come to church!'"

Mr. Silver Bell said to himself, "I hope a church buys me. I want to call people to worship God. I want to ring out, 'Ding! Dong! Come to church!'"

One day a minister came to the factory to buy a bell for the church. Mr. Red Bell and Mr. Silver Bell were brought out for him to choose. The minister looked and looked at them. They were both fine bells. Which one should he buy?

Mr. Red Bell whispered, "I hope he buys me."

Mr. Silver Bell whispered, "I hope he buys me."

At last the minister decided. "I believe I will buy the silver bell." How happy Mr. Silver Bell was! He had his wish. He was going to be a church bell.

Mr. Red Bell was sad at first, but then he said, "Perhaps another church will buy me."

Next day the mayor of the town came to the factory to buy a bell. As soon as he saw Mr. Red Bell, he said, "That is the bell I want." So the mayor bought Mr. Red Bell. He took him to a tall tower in the middle of the town.

The mayor had bought the red bell for all the children of the town. Any boy or girl who had a birthday could come to the bell and ring it. Then all the children would gather around the bell and sing, "Happy Birthday."

Mr. Red Bell loved the children and loved to have them ring him, but he was sad. He wanted to serve God, but no, he couldn't do that. Mr. Silver Bell was the church bell. Mr. Red Bell was only the birthday bell. How sad he felt.

It was almost Christmas when something very exciting happened. All the children gathered around Mr. Red Bell and said, "Christmas is coming soon, and Christmas is Jesus' birthday. When *we* have a birthday, we ring the red bell. On Christmas let's all come and ring the bell because it is Jesus' birthday."

How happy Mr. Red Bell was! He could ring out to tell everyone that it was Jesus' birthday. He could serve God, too.

On Christmas Day Mr. Red Bell rang out, "Ding! Dong! It's Jesus' birthday. Ding! Dong!"

Mr. Silver Bell rang out, "Ding! Dong! Come to church. Ding! Dong!"

The two bells rang out together. "Ding! Dong! Happy birthday! Merry Christmas! Ding! Dong!"

Now both Mr. Red Bell and Mr. Silver Bell were serving God. They were both very happy.

— —Shirley Miller

"He loved us, and sent His Son"
—I John 4:10.

The little Pine tree

At the edge of the forest stood a tall Spruce tree and close beside it grew a little Pine tree. The Spruce said, "One day I shall have to leave you, little Pine."

"Why?" asked the little Pine. "Did you not tell me the Lord set us here to beautify the earth?"

"It isn't enough to be beautiful," said the Spruce. "We must be useful. Perhaps that Oak tree will help to build a ship or a house. That Maple might become a child's bed."

"Well, *I* would rather stay here in the forest," said the little Pine.

When snow lay thick on the branches of the trees, many men came into the forest. But this time they took only evergreens.

"It is because Christmas is near," the Spruce explained. "Everywhere God's people are remembering the birthday of the Lord Jesus. And the trees have a part in making this a joyful time. People take us into their homes and hang bright ornaments and colored lights on our branches, to delight the hearts of little children."

"He loved us, and sent His Son"
—I John 4:10.

One day some men noticed the tall Spruce. "A splendid Christmas tree for the church!" they said. "Hear the wind murmur in its branches!"

But the little Pine knew it was only his friend whispering happily, "Good-by, little Pine, good-by! Don't be sad. One day you, too, may be chosen."

It was lonely at first. The little Pine wondered why the Spruce had been so willing to give himself simply to bring gladness to people. Then one day he thought, "Why, yes! God *made* us trees. How else can I thank Him for my life, except by serving in any way I can?"

So the little Pine hoped that he, too, would soon have a chance to serve. But he was such a little tree; too small to help build a house or even a child's bed. The men always passed him by.

Then a poor man came into the forest to find a Christmas tree for his children. But he kept shaking his head.

"*This* one is too wide to go through the doorway. *That* one is too tall."

The little Pine held its branches gracefully and waited. And *then* . . .

"Ah!" said the father. "Here is one that is just right!"

Carefully he carried the little Pine home and when it was trimmed it was a wonderful sight! On Christmas Eve the children gathered around to sing about the little Lord Jesus. And the little Pine trembled with gladness, for at last he understood what the tall Spruce had known so long—*that the only real joy is in giving.*

——AILEENE SARGENT

The train station

One afternoon, Petey's big brother Al said, "Put on your warm clothes, Petey. We'll go to see the trains."

Just as they reached the station, a big train came in. *Chug-a-chug-a-chug-a-choo. Whoo-oo-ooooooooot! Whsssss-sssssssssss.* As soon as the train stopped, people began to hop down from it. Men with suitcases hurried back and forth. When some of them bumped into Petey, they looked very cross!

Al tried to help Petey get out of the way of the busy men, but there were so many people, they didn't know which way to go. Petey felt like crying.

Just then they heard a big kind voice. "Come this way, boys." It was the train engineer! And in a moment, the big engineer had helped them out of the way of all the busy people.

"Some people are too busy all of the time, and other people are too busy some of the time," said the engineer, smiling at them. "There is only one Person never too busy for children."

"Is that you?" asked Petey.

"No," said the engineer. "Sometimes I have to be busy. But Jesus is never too busy for children. He wants to be the best Friend of all boys and girls. They can come to Him any time, and He's never too busy to listen to them."

Then the big engineer lifted both boys up to the engine room and in another moment had leaped up beside them. "I am not busy right now," he said. "I'll show you the engine."

What fun! Petey and Al tried on his engineer's hat and took turns sitting on the engineer's seat. They put their hands together on the whistle chain just right, and they pulled the whistle chain just a little bit and made it say *"Whoo-oo-oooot!*

Then the engineer helped them down to the station platform again. "I have to get busy again now," he said. "I have to take the train to the next place." Then, *Whsssssssssssssssss. Whoo-oo-ooooooooot! Chug-a-chug-a-chug-a-choo.* The train slowly left the station. Petey and Al stood on the platform and waved and waved until they couldn't see the big engineer any more.

Petey said, "He's our good friend, isn't he? He's our good engineer friend."

"Yes," answered Al. "He wasn't too busy to show us the train engine. But he said that Jesus is *never* too busy for us. He said that Jesus wants to be our best Friend."

"I know what!" said Petey, with a happy little laugh. "The engineer is our *good* friend, and Jesus is our *best* Friend."

Then Petey began to move his arms as though they were the wheels of the big train. *Whsssssssssssssssss,* said Petey. Al pretended to pull a whistle. *Whoo-oo-oooooooooo!* And they both went *Chug-a-chug-a-chug-a-choo,* all the way home.

— —WANDA SCHICKLING

"I have loved thee with an everlast — ing love" —Jeremiah 31:3.

In the hospital

Mother asked, "Where is the pain? Where does it hurt you, May?"

"Here," said May. "Right here on my side."

Soon a doctor came. He put two fingers on the place where it hurt. He pressed, and May cried "Ouch!"

The doctor said that May had a bad appendix. "We have a nice windup bed in the hospital for May. We'll take good care of her, and soon she'll be better."

The doctor said Mother might come with May in his car. At the hospital a nurse helped Mother to undress May and put a little white gown on her. Then May could climb into the clean white windup bed.

"Go to sleep, now," Mother said.

"Are you going to sleep here, too?"

"No, May. The doctor says I should go home tonight and come back in the morning. You can press this button if you need the nurse. And remember, the Lord Jesus is with you."

When May awoke early the next morning, Mother hadn't arrived yet. But a pretty nurse came in and helped May to wash. "I'm Miss Morning Nurse," she said, smiling. "I'll help you every morning while you're here."

"I have loved thee with an everlast — ing love" —Jeremiah 31:3.

Soon after Mother came, Miss Morning Nurse placed May on a table with wheels. She rolled the table to another room. There May saw the doctor again. But another nurse asked May to breathe a strange-smelling something. It made her feel sleepy, and she went to sleep. When she awoke, the doctor and Mother were standing beside her, smiling.

"You've just had an operation," said the doctor. "Your side will hurt you for a while, but you're going to be all well before long. And you're going to have a little scar! Think of that!"

Then May was taken back to her windup bed, and Miss Morning Nurse took care of her again. Each morning Miss Morning Nurse wound up May's windup bed so that May could sit up and look through the window or the door.

After a few days May was told that she could soon go home. Only one thing made her feel sad about it. "I wish you could go along with me," she told Miss Morning Nurse.

On the way home, May was thinking. "You know, Mother? When I was in the hospital, you couldn't stay with me all the time. Miss Morning Nurse was with me there, but she can't come home with us now. But I know *Somebody* who's always with me, don't I?"

"Who's that?" asked Mother.

"It's the Lord Jesus, isn't it?"

"Yes," said Mother, "whether we're sad or happy—or well or sick—or at home or at the hospital or any other place, God takes care of us all the time."

— —Wanda Schickling

The girl who found a Helper

"I'm naughty!" said Jean. "I need help to be good."

"It takes a strong person to make you good," said her friend.

So Jean went to see Mister Strong Man and told him she needed help. Mister Strong Man invited her into his back yard. There he lifted a heavy log high in the air with one hand. He chinned himself 50 times on a pole. He tore an old telephone book in two with his bare hands.

"Now, how can I help *you?*" asked Mister Strong Man.

Jean said, "I'm naughty! I need help to be good."

"Oh, I'm not strong enough to help you in *that* way," said Mister Strong Man. "Go to see Mister Fine Doctor."

So Jean went to the hospital and asked for Mister Fine Doctor and told him she needed help. Mister Fine Doctor took her to see some of his patients. First there was a sick man who felt better after taking some medicine given him by Mister Fine Doctor. Then there was a little boy who felt better after Mister Fine Doctor had given him a shot. Last there was a little girl who felt much better after Mister Fine Doctor had bandaged her sore leg.

"Strong is the Lord God"
—Revelation 18:8.

"Now, how can I help *you?*" asked Mister Fine Doctor.

Jean said, "I'm naughty! I need help to be good."

"Oh, I'm not able to give you *that* kind of help," said Mister Fine Doctor. "Go to see Mister Good President."

So Jean hurried to a big city. She went to Mister Good President's office and told him that she needed help. Mister Good President told her how much work he had to do and how many people he had shaken hands with the night before and how many letters were on his desk to sign that afternoon. "Now, how can I help *you?*" asked Mister Good President.

Jean said, "I'm naughty! I need help to be good."

"Oh, I'm not able to give you *that* kind of help," said Mister Good President. "But God is strong enough to give you that kind of help. You should go to Him."

Jean hurried home. She knelt beside her bed. She asked God, "Can *You* make me good?"

A still small voice seemed to remind Jean of a Bible verse, "Strong is the Lord God." Yes, it seemed that God was telling her that He could help her to be good because He is strong and able.

"Thank You, thank You," Jean sang to God.

Then she went to tell her friend, "Neither Mister Strong Man nor Mister Fine Doctor nor Mister Good President can make me good. But God can!"

——Wanda Schickling

16

Besides that!

"Come on!" Bim's daddy would call. "Get on my back, and I'll give you a piggy-back ride!" Then around the house and into the kitchen and right around Mother they would go, laughing and shouting. Bim was a big little boy to carry, but his daddy was strong.

Besides that, Bim's daddy could do a lot of other things. Why, he made a sled for Bim! It's a hard job to make a sled, and it takes a lot of work. But Bim's daddy was strong!

Besides that, Bim's daddy could lift or pull heavy things. One day, his daddy put Bim on a sled and pulled him him all the way to the sliding hill.

Seven blocks is a long way to pull a sled and a boy, but Bim's daddy was very strong!

When they got to the hill, Bim's daddy sat on the sled behind Bim. He put his big feet on the front steering part of the sled. He gave a little push with his hand, and

Whee-ee-ee-ee-ee-ee-ee-ee!

They skimmed down the hill so fast Bim could hardly see what was happening. He would have been afraid if his daddy hadn't been with him.

Then of course they had to walk

"Strong is the Lord God"
—Revelation 18:8.

back up the hill before they could come down again. And it was a very steep hill! Bim could hardly climb it. But his daddy could easily climb the steep hill and, besides that, pull the sled up behind him and, besides that, help Bim!

Bim said, "Daddy, when I get big I'm going to be just like you—because you're stronger than anybody in the whole world."

"No, I'm not, Bim. Lots of people are stronger than I. And besides that, Bim, there is God. God is stronger than everybody in the world put together!"

They reached the top of the hill, huffing and puffing. Bim's daddy pointed to the steep hill they had climbed. "See, Bim? A man couldn't make a hill like that unless he had a machine or a lot of other men to help him. But God made this hill and lots of other higher and bigger ones, all by Himself."

"And besides that," said Daddy, "God made the sky up above us and the wind and the snow."

"What else is there besides that?" asked Bim.

"Why, there are so many other things that it would take all kinds of talking to tell you. But one thing besides that, is this—God is so strong that He can help all His friends who love Him."

Then Bim smiled. "Besides that, Daddy, I'm one of His friends, and He helps me!"

"And besides that," said Daddy, "I'm one of His friends, too!"

Then they jumped on the sled again and went down the hill together.

Whee-ee-ee-ee-ee-ee-ee-ee-ee-ee!

——Wanda Schickling

One shiny coin

Daddy came home from work. He looked at the pieces of money from his pocket and picked out one. "See this shiny coin, Patsy?" he asked. "It is shiny because it is a new piece of money. Who would like to have this one shiny coin?"

"I would, Daddy," said Patsy.

Daddy put the one shiny coin into Patsy's open hand. With his big strong fingers he closed her small fingers around it. "You may do what you wish with this one shiny coin!"

It was such a silvery smooth shiny coin that Patsy didn't want to put it in her bank. So Mother gave her a handkerchief and showed her how to tie that one shiny coin in the corner.

Then Patsy put that handkerchief underneath her pillow. She liked that coin because it was silvery and smooth and because her Daddy had especially given it to her. Every day she untied the lovely handkerchief several times and looked at that one shiny coin.

On Sunday morning Patsy took the handkerchief with her one shiny coin tied in the corner. She took it to the church to show that one shiny coin to her teacher and to her friends. They all thought it was very pretty.

Then Teacher told Patsy and the other children about some small Indian boys and girls in South America who did not know about Jesus. Because their parents did not have a Bible, the boys and girls heard no stories of Jesus.

"What could we do to help that family?" asked Teacher.

The boys and girls thought for a moment. One boy said, "We could give some money to buy a Bible for them."

"Yes," said a girl, "we could help Jesus by giving."

Then Teacher brought out a pretty box. "I will help," she said, as she put in several coins. A boy put four coins in the box. A girl put two coins in. A boy put so many in that they couldn't count fast enough.

Patsy stood up. "Please, Teacher, would one shiny coin help?"

"Oh, yes!" answered Teacher. "One shiny coin would help!"

Patsy carefully unfolded the handkerchief, and from one corner she took her one shiny coin. "I'm helping Jesus by giving," she said with a smile as she put that one shiny coin in the box.

The next Sunday, Teacher brought a fine Bible purchased with all the coins the children had given. She would send it the next day to the family who did not have a Bible. Then the Indian boys and girls could hear stories of Jesus.

Teacher said, "Each one of you helped Jesus by giving what you could."

Patsy felt very happy. She said, "I gave my one shiny coin."

——WANDA SCHICKLING

"Even a child is known by his doings" —Proverbs 20:11.

The new neighbors

A big truck full of furniture came to the empty house next door. Next came a car full of people and a dog.

"I wonder if they'll like me," thought Patsy. "I *know* that Jesus likes me, but I wonder if the new neighbors will like me."

Their doggy was sniffing all over his new yard. Then he jumped to the sidewalk beside Patsy. He wagged his tail and wriggled.

"Oh, I think he likes me!" thought Patsy, as she threw a stick for the doggy to chase. "I *know* Jesus likes me, and I *think* the doggy likes me."

A very little boy came out of the house next door. Patsy said, "I'll give you a ride in my wagon."

The little boy didn't want to ride in Patsy's wagon. But he ran into his house and came back with a bright ball. "See?" He showed her the ball and smiled.

"Oh, I think he likes me!" thought Patsy. "I *know* Jesus likes me, and I *think* this little boy likes me."

Then Patsy began to push her wagon. But she fell and hurt her knee a little bit. A big girl ran out of the new neighbor's house. She helped Patsy to

"I have loved thee with an everlast — ing love"
—Jeremiah 31:3.

stand up. "There!" she said. "You're all right! What's your name?"

"Patsy."

"What a pretty name!" said the girl.

Patsy thought, "Oh, I think she likes me! I *know* Jesus likes me, and I *think* the big girl likes me."

Just as the mother and father came out of the house, Mother called, "Patsy, are you in the way over there?"

The mother of the new neighbors called back cheerfully, "No, she's just fine! She's not in our way!"

But Patsy wanted to run to her house, anyway. She had something to tell. "Mother! I *think* the new neighbors like me!"

"Why do you think so?" asked Mother.

"Their doggy wagged his tail, and their little boy showed me his ball, and their big girl helped me up and said my name was pretty, and their mother and father let me watch them move!"

Mother seemed pleased. "I'm so glad. But, Patsy, it's more important that Someone else loves you. Do you know whom?"

Patsy answered, "Mother, I *know* Jesus loves me! Do you know how I know, Mother? Because He came to earth for me, and because He takes care of me and stays with me everywhere I go, and because He likes to help me. *That's* how I know."

Mother gave Patsy a hug. "That's how I know that Jesus loves me, too, Patsy. And if you let Him help you, I know you'll have a nice time with the new neighbors." And Patsy did!

— —WANDA SCHICKLING

The noisy tick-tock clock

Everyone was happy because Mrs. Tillie was coming for a little visit. Mrs. Tillie knew how to make everyone laugh. Mother said, "If we had enough beds, Mrs. Tillie could stay with us for a week."

Dan said, "I can sleep on pillows on the floor, Mother. Then Mrs. Tillie can have my bed."

And so, Mrs. Tillie was asked to come for a week, and she came. The very first evening, she made everyone laugh. She told funny stories and jokes. She sang funny songs. She asked the children to tell the jokes they knew and sing the songs they knew. When it was time for bed, Mrs. Tillie told a story from the Bible.

Then Mrs. Tillie hung her clothes in the closet while Mother made Dan a bed of pillows on the floor and tucked him in.

Mrs. Tillie pulled a big clock from her suitcase. She put it on the chest beside her Bible. "I hope this noisy tick-tock clock won't bother Dan tonight," she said. "I've become used to hearing it tick, and I like to have it with me wherever I go."

"Speak, Lord, for Thy servant hears" —1 Samuel 3:9.

Dan soon went to sleep, but he awoke during the night after everyone else was asleep. The house was very quiet. He could only hear Mrs. Tillie's breathing and the noisy *tick-tock, tick-tock* of the noisy clock. He felt all alone; he felt alone in the dark. "I'm all alone," Dan said to himself. Then the noisy clock seemed to say it. Instead of *tick-tock, tick-tock,* the clock seemed to say *all-alone, all-alone, all-alone, all-alone.*

For a moment, Dan felt like calling his mother. Then he remembered to listen to God's voice. In a still small voice, God seemed to whisper deep, down inside of Dan a verse Dan had learned from the Bible, *He cares for you.*

"Jesus is right here with me," Dan thought. "He cares for me." Soon the clock seemed to be saying, *He cares for me, He cares for me, He cares for me, He cares for me.*

Soon Dan was fast asleep again. At breakfast time, everyone was laughing and having a good time with Mrs. Tillie. Then Mrs. Tillie thought of something. "Dan, did you hear my noisy tick-tock clock last night?"

"Yes," Dan said, smiling. "First it said, *you're all alone, all alone, all alone, all alone.* But after I listened to God, the clock said, *He cares for me, He cares for me, He cares for me, He cares for me.*"

Mrs. Tillie said, "I do like the ticking of that noisy tick-tock clock."

Dan said, "So do I! Especially after I've listened to God's voice."

——Wanda Schickling

Three lost nickels

Don put his hand into his pocket to make sure that three nickels were still there. He didn't know whether to feel good or not. Three nickels was really quite a bit. And no one even knew he had found them.

All the way to Sunday School he kept thinking about the money. He could buy the book about airplanes. And he'd have money left for ice cream too! Lots of other things he might decide to buy.

Yet Don didn't feel quite sure about it. The money wasn't really his. He had found it on the sidewalk just a block from church. It must have been somebody's because it was wrapped in a pink handkerchief. Maybe he should give part of it in the offering in the Beginner department. "That should make things right," he said. "Then I can keep the rest for myself."

When Don got to Sunday School, he told his friend Terry all about it. That sort of made him feel better.

"We want to welcome some new children this morning," said the teacher.

Two of the new girls sat in the same row with Don and Terry. During the story the girl next to Don began to make a funny noise. Don didn't look at her right away and pretended he didn't see her beginning to cry. The girl next to her handed her a hanky and she blew her nose hard.

Then Don whispered to her, "What's the matter? Don't you feel well?"

She shook her head. The other girl leaned over and said, "My sister lost some of her birthday money on the way to Sunday School. She was going to put it in the offering. She lost her handkerchief too."

Don didn't answer. After all, he wasn't sure that the money he found belonged to this new girl.

Don tried hard to listen. But there was something wrong. He felt very wiggly, as he listened to the story about Samuel, who obeyed God even when it was hard to obey. Don really did want to please Jesus, but sometimes it was hard.

"Don, will you and Terry please pass the offering basket today?" asked Teacher.

Don gulped. Then he said in what he expected to be a loud voice, but it turned out to be only a squeak, "But first I want to return something that I found!"

He handed the hanky with the money to the girl who sat next to him.

"Is this yours?"

"Oh, yes!" she cried. "Thank you!"

Don just smiled and joined Terry at the front of the classroom, to pass the offering basket. Sometimes right things are hard to do, he thought. But God helps us do them if we want to obey.

——Leona Choy

"Speak, Lord, for Thy servant hears"
—1 Samuel 3:9.

21

The very best Book

After Granny had visited Donna's house for a while, she went away. She sent a pretty teapot to Donna's mother and a crisp new five-dollar bill for Donna. "I would like to have Donna buy a nice book for herself with this money."

How happy Donna felt when Mother said she could choose the new book all by herself. "I want to find the very best book," she said. "Then I will ask Granny to read to me from it when she comes to visit us again."

One day Mother took Donna to the bookstore. Donna was surprised to see so many books, everywhere. "They make me dizzy," she said. Mother smiled.

When the clerk came to help them, Donna said, "I want to buy the very best book."

The clerk began to show her many books. One was about dogs. One was of horses. One was of dolls. One was a book of things to do. One was a book of little stories. One had stand-up pieces in it. One was of nursery rhymes.

Donna wished she could have all of them, and it was hard to make a choice. "I have to be sure I have the very best because I can only buy one," she told the clerk.

Then Donna saw a book that the clerk hadn't shown yet. "What book is that?" Donna asked. "It looks like the book my Sunday School teacher has."

"This book is a Bible." The clerk opened it to show Donna many pictures of Bible stories.

"My teacher says that the Bible is God's Book," said Donna. "God talks to people through the Bible. After you read God's words in the Bible, He talks to you, deep down in your heart."

"I read my Bible every day," said Mother. "If I could own only one book, I would choose the Bible."

Then Donna reached up and touched the Bible gently. "The Bible must be the best Book. This is the Book I want to buy with my five dollars."

The clerk handed the Bible to Donna and took Donna's crisp new money. Then Donna and Mother left the store and went home.

After a while, Granny came to visit again. She gave everyone a hug. After she hugged Donna, Donna said, "Granny, I found the best Book to buy with the money you sent me."

"What did you buy?" asked Granny.

"I bought a Bible. I chose it all by myself. And it is the best Book because God talks to people through it. After you learn God's words from the Bible, He talks to you, deep down in your heart."

"That's right," said Granny. "You did find the best Book, didn't you?"

Then Granny and Donna sat down together while Granny told Donna a Bible story from the very best Book, God's Word.

— —WANDA SCHICKLING

"Speak, Lord, for Thy servant hears" —I Samuel 3:9.

The beautiful pink cake

How good Mother's cake smelled! Tony and Tim kept wishing they could have some as soon as it came all hot from the oven. But instead, Mother first allowed it to cool. Then she covered it with fluffy pink frosting.

"Please, Mother, can't we have a piece now?" asked Tony.

Mother smiled. "I know it looks good. But I've told you before that my friends are coming this afternoon. Then we'll all have a piece together."

The cake looked like a beautiful pink lampshade. Tony and Tim just couldn't wait until afternoon! When Mother went out of the room, they ran to the cake. Each one drew one finger down the side of the cake. They popped the fluffy pink frosting into their mouths. O-oh—how good it tasted!

Mother came back in, and there were her two boys, licking their fingers. And the beautiful cake was no longer beautiful! Mother was so disappointed. "Now I must spend more time fixing the cake. You two boys must learn to mind Mother. Sit on these two chairs now for half an hour."

When the half hour was up, Mother called, "You may go and play now."

Instead, Tony said a very bad thing. He whispered, "Let's run away."

Tim asked, "Where'll we go?"

Tony answered, "Our Sunday School teacher likes us. She'll let us stay with her." So they took their tricycles. They pedaled a block and a half to the house where their teacher lived. "We've come to live with you," they told her. "Our mother punished us."

Then the twins told their teacher all about the beautiful cake. "We don't like it at our house any more."

Their teacher was sad. She said, "Don't be angry at your kind mother, Tony and Tim. Maybe you weren't listening to God's voice."

"What would God say to us about cake?" asked Tony.

"If we listen," their teacher said, "God reminds us of Bible verses we have learned. He reminds us in a still small voice—deep down inside of us. What verse do you think God would have reminded you of, if you had listened to Him before spoiling Mother's beautiful cake?"

Tim said, "I know. God would tell us, *'Children, obey your parents in the Lord.'* That's what God wanted to tell us, but we weren't listening."

"Let's go right home and tell Mother we're sorry," said Tony. They started off. When they reached home Mother seemed glad to see them. They told her, "We're sorry." Then Tim said, "I think we get along better if we listen to God's voice. Don't you think so, Tony?"

And Tony said—"YES!"

——Wanda Schickling

"Speak, Lord, for Thy servant hears" —I Samuel 3:9.

The little country church

Each Sunday Caroline went to Sunday School in a big church with tall rooms and people wherever she looked. Her Sunday School teacher said, "Here in our church we learn God's Word together. After God speaks to us through the Bible, if we listen, He reminds us of His words again, deep down inside."

Then one week end Caroline's mother and father decided to go to the country to visit some relatives. "You'll have a good time with your cousin Paul," they told Caroline.

And Caroline did have a good time! She and Paul went down the hill many times together on Paul's sled. They made a tunnel in the snow and a snow man. They had so much fun, they hated to stop playing, even for meals.

The next morning was Sunday morning. "Are we going to Sunday School?" asked Caroline.

"We don't have to," answered Paul. "This once we can stay home and play in the snow. But if you want to go to Sunday School we can."

Caroline went and looked out the window at their beautiful snow man. It would be such fun to build another one right beside it, with a long carrot nose. But then she thought about listening to

God's voice. "We can have fun in the snow this afternoon," she said. "Let's go to Sunday School this morning."

So Caroline and Paul got ready for Sunday School, and their parents did, too. They went in the car down the snow-filled road, in snowy tracks.

How surprised Caroline was when she saw the church! It wasn't a big church like the one in the city. Instead, it was a small white church with a white steeple and a bell high in the air. As Caroline and Paul stamped the snow off their feet on the porch, the bell seemed to be ringing, *"Good morning, God bless you. Good morning, God bless you."*

The two children went to a small cozy classroom where the teacher smiled at them. She taught from the Bible. "God speaks His words to you in the Bible," she said. "Then, if you listen to God, He will help you remember what He has said in the Bible. He'll talk to you, deep down inside."

The boys and girls sang a special song for Caroline to show her they were glad she had come to visit. And as all the people left the church, the bell seemed to be ringing, *"Good-by, God bless you. Good-by, God bless you."*

On the way back to Paul's house, Caroline said, "I'm glad we went to Sunday School instead of staying home to play. In the city I go to a big church and in the country to a little church. And God talks to me through His Word in both of them. I like to listen to God from His Book."

— —WANDA SCHICKLING

"Speak, Lord, for Thy servant hears" —I Samuel 3:9.

24

The castle game

Sometimes Bob and Barby didn't know what to play all day long. The girl from the apartment upstairs would go to school. But when she would come home she'd find many things for them all to play together.

"Let's play the castle game," Doris said one day. "I'll be the queen. Bob can be the king, and Barby can be the princess."

The table was their castle. They made a wall around it with chairs. Mother let them use her broom, her mop, and her dust mop as horses.

"What does the king do?" asked Bob.

"The king rules the country. And when he's not working, he rides around on his horse. If the people see him, they wave because he's good, and he's strong, and they love him."

"What does the queen do?"

"She sees that the castle is clean and neat, and she wears beautiful clothes, and everyone minds her. She's good, too."

"Well, what does the princess do?"

"She plays with all of her toys and goes to school and helps the queen."

Then they started the castle game. The king put on his coat and his crown. After that he went out on his dust mop horse to see that work was getting done on a domino bridge.

The princess had breakfast and then went to school. When she got home, the princess and the queen went riding on their horses—the broom and the mop.

They met the king behind the couch in the living room. All the pretend people were cheering and waving to them. After going through the park four times, they got hungry and went back to the castle for some cookies and milk.

And they did a lot of other things, too! It was a wonderful game, and they decided to play it the next day when Doris came home from school. Now she had to go upstairs for her dinner.

"Of course," said Doris sadly, "we don't know any real kings or queens or princesses. I wish we did."

"*We* know a real King," said Bob.

"Oh, no, you don't!" said Doris.

"Yes, we do!" said Barb. "He's the best King and the strongest King and the most wonderful King! And He's our Friend!"

"Does He wear beautiful clothes and a crown?" asked Doris.

"We don't know that," said Bobby. "But He's beautiful and shining because He's with God in heaven. He's Jesus."

Doris stood very still and quiet. "I know about Jesus," she said at last. "But I didn't know He was a King."

The twins smiled. "You see? We do know a real live King, and He's our Friend."

A smile came to Doris' face, too. "Then I know a King, too," she said, happily, "because Jesus is my Friend."

— —WANDA SCHICKLING

"With my song will I praise Him"
—Psalm 28:7.

25

The very little voice

Barby, who had a very little voice, didn't sing with the other children in her Sunday School. Though she knew the songs, she didn't sing.

After each song, someone would ask, "Did you sing, Barby?"

And Barby would answer in her very little voice, "No."

The children were very anxious to have Barby sing with them. They hoped that sometime she would.

One day Teacher brought a lovely picture showing children of long ago waving palm leaves and singing songs of praise to Jesus.

A girl said, "I wish we could have been with those children. Jesus heard their singing, and it pleased Him."

A boy said, "We can sing to Jesus right here. He can hear us."

Barby began to speak slowly in her very little voice. "Could Jesus hear me if I sang?"

"Yes," answered Teacher. "Jesus could hear you. And it pleases Him to hear sweet praises from every kind of voice, even a very little one."

Then Teacher asked if the children would like to go out of the room to the hall and come back singing, pretending they were the children of the picture. She brought out cardboard pretend harps some children had made. She brought pretend palm leaves, cut from green paper. The children chose palm leaves or harps and went out to the hallway.

Barby went quietly out with the others, holding a pretend palm leaf. She felt very happy because she was thinking, "Jesus can hear me if I sing, and I can please Him as other children do with songs of praise."

When Teacher began to play the piano, the children began to walk back into the room. The pretend palm leaves waved in the air. The pretend cardboard harps made beautiful pretend music. The children sang the real song of praise they had chosen:

I will sing like David,
I will sing, I will sing;

And Barby, with her very little voice, was also singing:

I will sing like David,
I will sing to God.

When the song of praise was finished the children went to their seats.

"Did you sing, Barby?" asked someone.

"Yes," answered Barby, in her very little voice.

"We didn't hear you," they said.

Barby felt very happy. She felt like singing the song of praise to God all over again. She said in her very little voice, "Jesus heard me, and He was pleased."

———WANDA SCHICKLING

"With my song will I praise Him" —Psalm 28:7.

Billy's biggest smile

Since Billy had been very very sick for a long long while, he didn't smile very often. But sometimes when his three older brothers told him special things, he would smile a *little*. And sometimes he would smile a *little more!* And for something very, very, very, very, very special—he would smile *his biggest smile!*

One day Billy's first older brother came home from Sunday School, very excited. "Billy, do you remember that green lily plant in the church hallway? Today it had a great big white lily flower on it. And Teacher says more flowers are coming!"

Billy could hardly believe it. "How did it happen?" he asked.

"Teacher says that God made the lily plant live and grow big and make the beautiful white flower. Isn't that special, Billy?"

"Yes," Billy answered. "It's special." And he smiled a *little*.

The next Sunday his second older brother came home from Sunday School, very excited. "Billy, you can't guess what happened in our room to-day. Remember that fuzzy little caterpillar we took to Sunday School, the one that went to sleep in a cocoon?"

"Yes?" Billy liked caterpillars!

"Today that caterpillar crawled out of the cocoon. But, Billy, he isn't a caterpillar any more. He has turned into a beautiful butterfly!"

"But how did it happen?" asked Billy.

"God made it happen, Billy. It's very special, don't you think?"

"Yes, it's very special," answered Billy, and he smiled. Not just a *little,* but a *little more!*

The next Sunday, Billy's third older brother came home from Sunday School, very excited. "Billy, remember how some angry men killed Jesus?"

"Yes, I remember," answered Billy. "He couldn't be with His friends then because He was dead."

"We had a wonderful Bible story to-day, Billy. And Jesus didn't stay dead; He's alive again and can be with all His friends, wherever they are."

"Can He be right here with us?" asked Billy. "We're His friends."

"He *is* right here with us!" said his third older brother. "Because He's alive now He's always with His friends."

"But, how did this happen?"

"God made Jesus alive again!" said the third older brother. "Isn't that very, very, very, very, very special?"

"Yes," answered Billy. "It's very, very, very, very, very special." And he *smiled*. Not a little *smile*. Nor a *little more*.

Billy *smiled his biggest smile*.

— —WANDA SCHICKLING

"He is risen"
—Mark 16:6.

27

The busy day

When Samuel opened his eyes that morning, he remembered that it was the day of the party. It was going to be a wonderful and busy day! And he felt like talking to God about it.

"Make it a nice party for Sister," he prayed. "And help me to be a good helper today because it's going to be a busy day."

Then he called to Sister. "Good morning! Wake up, Sleepyhead. Happy birthday!"

When Sister awoke and smiled at him, Samuel jumped up and dressed himself. Dressing himself was always a help to Mother, and she smiled a special smile of thanks when she saw Samuel all dressed. "That's a big help for me on such a busy day," she said.

After Sister went to school, Samuel and Mother were very busy. Samuel hid peanuts for the peanut game. He helped Mother blow up some balloons. He helped her fold party napkins.

"What else can I do to help?"

Mother asked, "Would you please dust the tables and chairs?"

Samuel didn't like to dust. He was about to say that he wouldn't dust. But then he talked to God about it. "This is such a busy day for Mother—even though I don't feel like doing it—please help me, God, to dust."

When Samuel finished the dusting, Mother's special smile of thanks told Samuel how pleased she was. "What a big help you are," she said.

Then Sister and the children came from school for the party. They were laughing and having a good time. They were full of fun.

Then they all had fun playing games. Samuel played, too. They played a balloon-blowing game. They played a look-for-peanuts game. They played a skip-to-music game. What fun!

After Sister had opened the presents brought by the children, Mother called everyone to the pretty table. There Sister blew out eight gleaming candles. Then the children ate birthday cake with ice cream and fruit punch.

It was oh, oh, oh, so much fun! But Samuel began to feel tired and then he began to feel cross. He talked to God about it. "Please help me be nice," he prayed. And God did help him, even though he still felt tired.

When all the children had left, Sister gave Mother a big hug. "Thank you, Mother, for the wonderful party."

Mother said, "Thank Samuel, too. He was really a big help on this busy day."

So Sister gave Samuel a big hug, too. "Thank *you*, Samuel."

Mother helped Samuel into his pajamas. And then Samuel knelt to say good night to the Lord. "Thank *You*, God, for the nice party and the nice day."

— —WANDA SCHICKLING

"I am with you alway"
—Matthew 28:20.

The big slide

One spring morning the April wind was warm instead of cold, and Jody's big brother said that he was going to the playground to play baseball.

"May I go, too?" asked Jody.

"Oh, I guess so," said Carl, "if you'll play with the smaller children and let me play ball."

Jody said she would, so they set out together. On the way, Jody said, "I think I'm big enough to go on the big slide now. Don't you think so?"

"Maybe," answered Carl.

There were many children at the playground. Some were swinging on very low swings. Some were swinging on big swings. Some were teeter-tottering. Some were climbing on the bars. Some were on the small slide.

And some were on the big slide! They were up at the top—and, *swish!* they were at the bottom.

Swish! Swish! Swish!!!

"Maybe I can do it," thought Jody.

As Carl went to the other side of the playground to play ball, Jody got in line behind the big slide. One by one she climbed the steps behind the other children. She felt excited. Up, up she went.

But when she reached the top of the steps, suddenly she didn't want to go

"I am with you alway"
—Matthew 28:20.

down the big slide. It looked too far down to the bottom. It was too long. She was up too high.

"Go down!" called all the children waiting on the steps below her.

"No, no!" answered Jody.

"Go on down because we want our turns," called the children. "We want to slide! Go down!"

Jody felt frightened. Then she remembered that she could talk to God anywhere. Inside her mind she prayed, "Please help me, God."

Just then Jody saw Carl running to the slide from the baseball field. As he came, he called, "What's the matter?"

"She won't go down," grumbled the children.

Quickly Carl climbed up past the children. "Don't be afraid, Jody. I'll help you." He put one arm around Jody and then got his legs onto the slide, around her. "We'll go down together," he said.

Swish!!! They were down!

Jody began to laugh. "I'm not afraid now!" she said. All the other children began to laugh with her. And, *Swish! Swish!! Swish!!!* Three more children came down safely.

Jody tried the big slide once more, and as she climbed she asked the Lord to help her not to be afraid. *Swish!!!* There she was again. She had come down the big slide all by herself.

As Carl ran back to the baseball field, Jody whispered to God, "Thank You, heavenly Father. Thank You for sending Carl to help me. And thank You for helping me not to be afraid."

— —WANDA SCHICKLING

Me too!

One day Ginny looked out a window and saw all her big friends in Helen's yard, next door. Helen was crying, and the other children seemed to feel unhappy, too.

Mother said Ginny could go over there, so she hurried to Helen's yard and asked what was the matter.

A boy said, "Her new blue bicycle that her father bought last week is gone! She left it out last night."

Helen's mother came to the door. "You must go and see if you can find the bicycle, Helen. And then you must remember from now on to put all your playthings away at night."

"We'll help you look!" suggested several children.

"Yes, we'll help!" said another. "We can go in different directions."

"Me too?" asked Ginny.

The big children turned and looked down at Ginny. One said, "Your mother wouldn't let you come."

Another said, "We are going to stay away a long time, perhaps."

Another said, "We are going to walk too fast for you."

That made Ginny feel sad, because she wanted to help Helen, too. When she saw everyone hurrying out of the yard, leaving her all alone, she began to cry.

But Helen came running back. "Don't cry. You *can* do something."

Ginny felt better. "What?"

"It says in the Bible that we should pray for one another," Helen said. "You can't come with us, but you can help by praying. Will you?"

"Oh, yes!" said Ginny, happily.

"Please don't cry any more," called Helen as she hurried away. Then it was very, very quiet in Helen's yard with only a bird chirping.

Ginny went back to her own yard and sat down on the steps of the porch in the warm sunshine. And she prayed. "Please help them find the new blue bicycle, God. And teach Helen to put her things away at night as her mother says."

She waited for a long time, and she kept praying. Then Mother called her in for lunch.

Just as she finished the last bite, she heard happy voices. Mother said she could run to Helen's house, so she did. And there was the new blue bicycle! Three of the big friends had found it in the yard of a boy just a block away. "His mother didn't know he had it," they said.

"Oh, what good friends you are!" Helen said.

"Me too?" asked Ginny.

"Yes, *you too!*" Helen said as she gave Ginny a hug. "They helped me by looking, and you helped by praying."

— —WANDA SCHICKLING

"Pray one for another"
—James 5:16.

Elizabeth Jones

Every morning and every afternoon, after all the other Jones children had gone to school, Mrs. Jones would send Elizabeth Jones to the post office.

Elizabeth was four years old and she didn't go to school *this* year, but she would go to school *next* year. And it was always Elizabeth who went to the post office to mail letters or to bring some letters back to Mother. She went down the hill and across a piece of pavement and up the steps and into the post office.

You see, all the Joneses were waiting and praying for the time that their daddy would write to say he could come home again. He had been sick in a far-away hospital for a long time. And they had been praying for him for a long time.

Down the hill went Elizabeth Jones every morning and every afternoon. Down the hill went Elizabeth Jones, and across the piece of pavement and up the steps and into the post office. "Do you have any mail for the Joneses?"

Sometimes the clerk said, "No, we don't have any mail for the Joneses."

Sometimes the clerk would say, "Yes, we do have some mail for the Joneses."

When there was no mail, Elizabeth Jones would go out of the post office and walk down the steps and walk across the piece of pavement and walk back up the hill to her house.

But if there were some mail, Elizabeth would walk out of the post office and then *run* down the steps and across the pavement and *run* up the hill to her house.

And sometimes the mail was from Daddy! When there was good news that Daddy felt better, Mother and Elizabeth would stop right there in the kitchen and thank the Lord.

If Daddy said in his letter that he didn't feel quite so well as before, Mother and Elizabeth would stop right there in the kitchen and ask the Lord to help Daddy get well.

Oh, yes, Mother Jones and Elizabeth Jones, and all the other Joneses kept right on praying and praying and waiting and waiting and praying.

One day, Elizabeth Jones went down the hill and across the pavement and up the steps and into the post office. "Is there any mail for the Joneses?"

"Yes, there is," said the clerk, who handed her the letter.

Elizabeth Jones walked out of the post office and *ran* down the steps and across the piece of pavement and *ran* up the hill to Mother Jones, who opened the letter quickly and—guess what?

"Daddy is coming home," said Mother Jones. "He is better."

Oh, yes! Mother Jones and Elizabeth Jones, and all the other Joneses had been praying for a long time. And God had answered their prayers.

————WANDA SCHICKLING

"Pray one for another"
—James 5:16.

31

Lost and found Judy

Judy's mother and father wanted Judy to learn her whole name and her address. "If you are ever lost, you can tell people who you are and where you live. Then they can bring you back home or help us find you."

Judy tried hard to learn, but it was difficult. Her mother said, "Ask the Lord to help you remember."

Father added, "And, Judy, wherever you go or whatever happens to you, the Lord is always with you."

One day, Judy's mother said, "Today is your birthday. Let's go downtown to buy you a birthday dress."

"I would like a pink one," said Judy.

She and Mother walked to a trolley bus and climbed up and in. Mother allowed Judy to put the money into the bus driver's fare box. It jingled.

Then the trolley bus bounced along to the center of town. Mother and Judy climbed off and went through some fast-turning doors into a big store.

"Hang onto my hand, Judy," said Mother. "Don't get lost."

There were trillions and billions of beautiful things everywhere in the big store. There were just as many people moving in all directions. Judy held tightly to Mother's hand.

"I am with you alway"
—Matthew 28:20.

First they went to a dress shop. Together they chose a lovely pink birthday dress for Judy. Then they bought candles for a birthday cake.

Soon after that Judy let go of Mother's hand—just for a moment. She picked up a pretty piece of paper. Then she hurried and put her hand into someone's hand. But that someone looked down, surprised, because it wasn't Mother. Judy quickly pulled her hand back and looked for Mother's hand, but she couldn't see Mother. She began to run about, looking and looking, but she could not see Mother.

"Jesus is with me," Judy reminded herself. "I don't need to be afraid because Jesus is always with me."

A kind lady took Judy to the Lost and Found department of the store. The man there smiled at Judy and asked, "What's your name and address?"

At first Judy couldn't remember. She prayed. *Then* she remembered! "My name is Judy Elizabeth Johnson and I live at 145 Arch Street!"

The man began to talk into a microphone. Soon Mother came hurrying to find her and hug her.

That night, Judy wore her new pink birthday dress. She blew out the four candles on her birthday cake! Then the whole family had ice cream and birthday cake as Judy and Mother told Father how Judy had been lost and found.

"And did you remember your name and address?" asked Father.

Judy smiled. "I asked the Lord to help me remember. And He did and then I did!"

——Wanda Schickling

32

Judy's shoe

Though Judy had on her new shoes, she could go for a walk with Tommy and even play awhile—if she would be careful of her new white shoes.

"I like to play with you, Tommy," said Judy, "because you are good to everybody. You're always good to me."

"It's because I love Jesus," said Tommy. And they started on their walk. They knew a girl on the other side of the block whose name was Patsy. Patsy had a sandbox.

Judy was ever so careful of her new white shoes, and they passed the first house and the second house and the corner house with the white fence. They turned the corner, went under the tall tree with red berries dropping from it, and saw Patsy playing in her sandbox with another girl. Then they hurried. "May we play?"

"Yes," answered Patsy, sweetly.

But the other girl whispered loudly, "Don't let them play."

"Yes, they may play," answered Patsy.

Judy took off her new shoes, and Tommy took off his shoes, and they placed them carefully beside the sandbox. Then they climbed over the edge

"Let us do good unto all"
—Galatians 6:10.

and sat down in the soft sand. They squished the sand through their toes.

Patsy and Judy and Tommy began to make a lovely sand-castle, with a road and a bridge. But the other girl pouted and said she wouldn't play. She went into a corner and made a sand hill all by herself.

When Patsy's mother called her, the other girl hurried home. Judy and Tommy went home, too. But Judy began to cry, "One of my nice new shoes is gone!" Yes! Beside the sandbox they saw Tommy's shoes and only one white shoe!

Judy looked around the sandbox and in the green grass in the yard. She could not find the shoe.

Tommy said, "I'll help you look." He put his hand in several places in the sandbox but did not find the shoe. Then he crawled to the corner where the other girl had built her sand hill. He put his hand in and pulled the shoe out! "Here is where that naughty girl hid your shoe!" he said.

Soon they were walking back home. Judy was ever so careful of her new white shoes, and they went under the tall tree with red berries dropping from it. They turned the corner and went by the corner house with the white fence and passed the second house and the first house. They came to the house where Tommy lived, which was right next to the house where Judy lived.

"You helped me find my shoe," said Judy. "You're always good to everybody. You're always good to me."

"It's because I love Jesus," said Tommy.

— —Wanda Schickling

It was Martha!

It was Martha who heard the telephone ring! She told Mother, who was hanging clothes outside. Mother ran in to answer the phone and then asked, "Oh, Martha, what shall I do? Daddy is bringing an old friend home for dinner tonight. How can I finish hanging up the clothes, take care of Baby, go after groceries, and also get a nice dinner ready?"

It was Martha who said, "I'll help, Mother. I'll do whatever I can."

Mother hugged her. "You are such a good daughter to help me as you do."

Martha said, "It's because I love Jesus."

And so, it was Martha who handed the clothespins to Mother, who then quickly pinned all the clothes on the line.

And when the Baby awoke, it was Martha who found his shoes and helped to dress Baby in his red suit.

It was Martha who climbed up in the car all by herself and closed the door and rolled the windows down.

When Mother stopped the car at the big grocery store, it was Martha who stayed in the car with Baby. She clapped her hands and sang songs. Yes, it was Martha who kept Baby from crying.

Mother soon returned with her arms full of groceries. It was Martha who opened the back door of the car for Mother. It was Martha who picked up —and put back in the box—all the berries that spilled when the car started.

When they reached home, it was Martha who helped carry the groceries into the house.

It was Martha who brought the big stirring spoon from the table drawer when Mother needed it. And it was Martha who brought the salt box from the cupboard and two eggs from the refrigerator. It was even Martha who washed the big mixing bowl that Mother needed for shortcake.

The afternoon passed quickly by. But when Father and his old friend arrived, a lovely dinner awaited them. Baby was neatly dressed in his little suit. How pretty Mother looked in her green dress. Martha wore her pink ruffly dress.

Father looked pleased when he saw the table. "Who helped you to get such a nice dinner ready?" he asked.

"It was Martha!" said Mother. "It was Martha who helped me all afternoon, because she loves Jesus."

Father and his friend smiled down at Martha. Then the friend brought from behind his back a lovely storybook. He said, "Here is a surprise for a good helper."

It was Martha who said, "Thank you!"

And who heard a story after dinner from the bright new book?

It was Martha!

—— WANDA SCHICKLING

"Let us do good unto all"
—Galatians 6:10.

Who will? I will!

Daddy stood in the open door with his brown briefcase. Outside, the triplets saw a taxi drive up. Daddy hugged everyone and asked, "Who will help Mother while I'm away?"

"I will," said John.

"I will," said Ron.

"I will," said Don.

Because they loved Jesus, they all wanted to help. They waved good-by as Daddy was taken away in the taxi.

Next morning the triplets had pancakes and syrup for breakfast. After breakfast Mother asked, "Who will help do the dishes?"

"I will," said John.

"I will," said Ron.

"I will," said Don.

Because they loved Jesus, they all wanted to help. Mother washed the dishes in hot soapy water; John and Ron wiped them. Don put them neatly on the proper cupboard shelves.

One afternoon Mother put on a fresh cotton dress and asked, "Who will come with me to help carry groceries home?"

"I will," said John.

"I will," said Ron.

"I will," said Don.

Because they loved Jesus, they all wanted to help. They went with Mother to the store and walked back with arms full of bags with many good things in them. When they arrived home, Mother asked, "Who will help make a welcome-home cake for Daddy?"

"I will," said John.

"I will," said Ron.

"I will," said Don.

Because they Loved Jesus, they all wanted to help. John got the cake mix. Ron connected the beater. Don got out the milk. Mother poured the batter into a pan and placed the pan in the heated oven.

When a taxi stopped again out in the front, the triplets all shouted and went to meet Daddy. He hugged them all and they all went into the house.

Daddy greeted Mother and asked, "Who helped you while I was away?"

Mother answered, "John did and Ron did and Don did! They all helped me, because they love Jesus." Then her eyes seemed to twinkle.

"Now who will help?" asked Mother.

"I will!" said John.

"I will!" said Ron.

"I will!" said Don.

Father looked very puzzled. "Help to do what?" he asked.

Mother and John and Ron and Don all shouted together, "Help to eat up your welcome-home cake!"

And they did!

— —WANDA SCHICKLING

"Let us do good unto all"
—Galatians 6:10.

How Hilty helped

Hilty's grandmother was coming that afternoon. Hilty and Hilty's cousin were going to help Jesus by doing what they could for Grandmother. And they would all go that evening to the Children's Day program at church.

But Hilty fell off the stairs by the front door and hurt her arm. She cried! When her mother and father saw that the arm was badly hurt, Father hurried with Hilty to the doctor.

"Broken?" asked Hilty's father.

"Broken," answered the doctor.

"Broken?" asked Hilty's mother, when Hilty came home with her arm in a sling.

"Broken!" Hilty answered proudly.

"But how can you help Grandmother?" asked Hilty's cousin.

"Oh, oh, oh!" said Hilty. She hadn't thought of *that!* "Oh, oh, oh!"

"Don't cry," said Hilty's cousin. "You can find some other way to help."

Hilty felt better. "I can sing!" she said. "I can help by singing!"

When Grandmother arrived, Hilty's cousin helped her to unpack and brought things she needed. Then Grandmother sat down to rest in a chair. Hilty said, "I can sing for you, Grandmother. I can help by singing!"

How Grandmother enjoyed those songs that Hilty had learned in Sunday School! They helped her to think of God.

That night, Hilty and Hilty's cousin and Hilty's father and mother and her grandmother went to church. The children looked at Hilty's arm.

"Broken?" asked Teacher.

"Broken!" answered Hilty.

"But how will you hold the big Bible picture so everyone can see?"

"Oh, oh, oh!" said Hilty. She hadn't thought of *that!* "Oh, oh, oh!"

"Don't cry," said Hilty's cousin. "You can find some other way to help."

Hilty felt better. She asked Teacher, "Could I help Jesus by singing?"

The program started. Some children told Bible stories. Some gave the verses they knew, so clearly that everyone could hear. Hilty's cousin and some other children held big Bible pictures with both hands, high up so that everyone could see. Some helped by singing.

Hilty helped by singing!

When the program was over, Hilty and Hilty's cousin and Hilty's mother and father and her grandmother went home together in Hilty's father's car.

Hilty's father and mother and Hilty's grandmother said they had learned something about God at the program.

Hilty's cousin said, "I helped Jesus by holding a big Bible picture."

And Hilty said, "I helped Jesus by singing!"

— —WANDA SCHICKLING

"Even a child is known by his doings" —Proverbs 20:11.

36

The thumpy sounds

To get a jar of cucumber pickles from the basement shelf, Timothy must go carefully down the wooden steps and carefully around the bucket and the old baby buggy. Then he must take the jar of cucumber pickles in both hands.

One day, just as Timothy put both hands around the jar of pickles, he heard strange sounds above him.

Thump, thump, thump!
Thump, thump, thump, thump, thump!!

Timothy felt very frightened! And after that day he would not go down into the basement alone any more.

One day Mother was especially busy. Because he loved Jesus, Timothy had done all he could that day to help her. Before supper Mother asked, "Timothy, please, please go down and bring up a jar of pickles. I'm so busy!"

Timothy knew that God wanted him to do as Mother asked, but he was afraid! Then it seemed as though God spoke to him in a still small voice. It seemed as though God reminded him of a good Bible story about David. David, too, had been afraid; but he obeyed and trusted God; and God had helped him.

"God will help me, too," thought Timothy. "If I obey and trust Him, God will help me, too."

Then Timothy went to the basement door. He went carefully down the wooden steps. He went carefully around the bucket and the old baby buggy. He put both hands around a smooth jar of good cucumber pickles.

Thump, thump, thump!
Thump, thump, thump, thump, thump!!

How frightened Timothy felt! "Oh, I'm so glad God is here to help me," he thought. "And I'm so glad Mother is up there in the kitchen."

Thump, thump, thump!
Thump, thump, thump, thump, thump!!

Suddenly Timothy began to laugh! He knew what the strange thump sounds were! He laughed as he carried the jar of cucumber pickles around the old baby buggy, around the bucket, and up the wooden steps. He laughed as he handed the jar of cucumber pickles to Mother, who smiled a pleased smile and said, "Thank you, Timothy."

"Mother, do you know what?" asked Timothy. "You make strange thump sounds down in the basement when you walk up here in the kitchen!"

"I do?" Mother seemed surprised.

"Yes!" said Timothy. "I was afraid to go down in the basement to get the pickles for you. But I did what God wanted me to do, and I trusted Him, and He helped me. I'm not afraid any more of the *thump, thump, thump, thump, thumpy* sounds!"

— —WANDA SCHICKLING

"Even a child is known by his doings" —Proverbs 20:11.

37

The high-up doorbell

Rudy watched Jack getting ready. He said, "I want to go, too."

"You're too little," said Jack.

Mother said, "Never mind, Rudy. You aren't too little to do something for Jesus."

"What can he do?" Jack asked.

Rudy thought for a while. "I can ring Mrs. Royce's doorbell and ask her and Billy to come to church with us. I don't think they know much about Jesus."

Jack laughed. Mrs. Royce's doorbell was so high that hardly any child could ring it. He said, "You're much too little to ring that high-up doorbell!"

"I'll try," answered Rudy, "because that's what I want to do for Jesus."

Rudy went to Mrs. Royce's house. He saw the bell, high up on the door. He asked God to help him reach it.

He put his fingers up and tried to reach it. But he couldn't.

He stood on tiptoe and put his fingers

"Even a child is known by his doings" —Proverbs 20:11.

up and tried to reach it. But he couldn't

He found a small board on the porch. He brought the board and stood on it on tiptoe and put his fingers up and tried to reach it. But he couldn't.

He went home and borrowed an old chair from his mother. Though the chair was heavy, Rudy carried it up the steps to the porch. He set it underneath the bell. Then he climbed up on the chair. He stood on tiptoe and tried to reach the bell. *He reached it!*

He pressed the small black button and heard the doorbell ringing in Mrs. Royce's house. Then he waited. He heard footsteps coming to the door. When Mrs. Royce opened the door and saw Rudy standing on the chair, she had a good laugh. "What a great deal of work you did to reach my doorbell!" she exclaimed. "You must have wanted to ring it very much!"

"Yes," said Rudy, smiling, "because I want to ask you and Billy to come to church with us on Sunday. You could learn about my best Friend, Jesus."

"Perhaps we will," answered Mrs. Royce. "Won't you come in?"

Then Rudy went into Mrs. Royce's house and played nicely with little Billy and talked with Mrs. Royce and ate two cookies with sugar on top.

Then Rudy carried the heavy chair back home. When he saw that Jack, too, was home, Rudy said, "I did!"

"You did what?" asked Jack.

"I reached Mrs. Royce's doorbell! And I think she will come to church with us soon. She wants to know more about my good Friend, Jesus."

— —Wanda Schickling

The little red wagon

On the morning of her fifth birthday June hurried through the kitchen to the porch. There on the porch was a little red wagon! Both Mother and Father shouted, "Happy birthday! Happy birthday!"

Then Father carried the little red wagon out to the sidewalk where June pulled it back and forth a while before breakfast. It made her feel very happy to own a little red wagon.

After breakfast Father took his lunch pail and went to work. Mother checked the cupboard and said she must go to the grocery store.

June thought how nice it would be to please Jesus and Mother by helping with her little red wagon. "I'll pull the groceries home for you," she said. Mother smiled and said that would be nice. They went to the store.

On the way home June pulled the little red wagon full of jars and boxes, bags and cartons. She and Mother pulled together when they crossed the streets. And it made June feel very happy to know she could please Jesus and Mother by helping.

They stopped at the shoe store and went in. June stared at the lines and lines of shoes on the shelves. She sniffed the strange smells and heard whirring noises as the shoe repair man brought some shoes to the counter. "All fixed!" he said, as he wrapped up two pair of Father's shoes and one pair of Mother's shoes and one of June's shoes with the strap sewed on again.

Mother paid the man and started to carry the heavy package. But June said, "I'll take it in my little red wagon."

Mother smiled and said that would be nice. It made June feel so very happy to know that she could please Jesus and Mother by helping.

When Father came home that evening, June ran and jumped up in his arms. "I like my little red wagon!"

"Good!" said Father. "Then how about a little ride around the block?" They went out. Father helped June into the wagon and away they went! Some of the time they went fast, and some of the time they went slow. Sometimes they went bump, bump, over the big cracks, and once they went so fast around the corner that June had to hold on tight. When they came back June was laughing and Father was huffing and puffing and laughing.

And Mother was putting pink candles on a round birthday cake with white and pink frosting.

One, two, three, four, five!

Oh, it made June feel so especially happy to have a birthday and a birthday cake and five candles and a ride around the block and Father and Mother and . . . *a little red wagon to help with!*

— —WANDA SCHICKLING

"Even a child is known by his doings"   —Proverbs 20:11.

39

Gumdrops for Harry

"I'm going grocery shopping with Mother!" shouted Harry, running as fast as his brown shoes could carry him.

While Mother waited, Harry scrubbed his face until it was really shiny. A short walk down one street and there they were.

How exciting it was to push along the cart while Mother loaded groceries into it!

"You must not touch a thing here, Harry," Mother explained. "Nothing belongs to us until we pay for it."

That was hard. Harry wanted to feel the smooth jars of jam piled high on a shelf. But just as his hand reached for one he remembered that God wanted him to obey what he was told. He put his hand into his pocket again. He felt good inside.

At the next counter there were boxes of cakes with cellophane-covered windows. What fun it would be to press a finger against the cellophane. But into his pocket went Harry's finger again.

Mother was finished and the cashier was checking her packages. Harry waited near the candy rack. His favorite gumdrops! Harry stepped closer with his back toward the gumdrops. No one was looking. Suddenly a box of gumdrops just "happened" to get into his pocket!

Harry's face felt hot. He looked around. His heart pounded hard.

"Come, Harry," called Mother. "We must hurry home to make dinner."

Harry dragged his brown shoes slowly across the floor. He didn't want to look at Mother. She stooped to put her arm around him.

Suddenly Harry pulled the gumdrops from his pocket. Mother just looked at him.

Then she said quietly, "Do you want to give them back?"

Harry nodded his head hard.

Mother and Harry walked hand in hand to the cashier and Harry gave her the gumdrops.

"I'm very sorry," Harry said, with tears spilling down his cheeks.

At first the cashier looked puzzled, then she smiled and put the box back on the candy rack.

"Mother, I guess I didn't listen to the voice of the Lord *every* time—just *part* of the time," said Harry.

"But why didn't you ask me for gumdrops?" said Mother pulling two packages of gumdrops from her bag.

"Oh, Mother! Thank you!" exclaimed Harry.

He began to feel good inside again. Next time he would remember that obeying the voice of the Lord *all the time* was better than doing wrong.

——Leona Choy

"Obey the voice of the Lord"
—Jeremiah 26:13.

Sandra decides

Sandra pouted as Mother called her for breakfast. "I'm not going to Sunday School!" she said.

Mother went down the stairs, humming. Soon the smell of toast came up to Sandra's nose.

"Hey Mom, where's the shoe polish?" shouted John from his bedroom. "I want my shoes to look good for Sunday School."

Sandra kept looking at her picture books and trying not to listen.

Daddy poked his head into Sandra's room and made a funny face.

"Hope the boys and girls in the Sunday School class that I teach aren't as slow as you are." Daddy left whistling.

Sandra looked out the window. It would be nice to play outdoors anyway.

"But I'm still staying home," she said aloud. "No Sunday School."

In the kitchen she met Grandpa, who was just sitting down at the table.

"What's our Bible verse for the Lord's Day, Sandra?" he asked.

Since Sandra didn't answer right away, John piped up, " 'I was glad when they said unto me, Let us go into the house of the Lord.' Is that right?" John took the last bite of his toast and just

"Obey the voice of the Lord"
—Jeremiah 26:13.

missed getting strawberry jam on his clean white shirt.

"Ga-Ga!" added Baby Jean, and they all laughed at her trying to talk too.

"I'm going to take Baby Jean to the Church nursery this morning," said Mother. "I know she will love God's house soon too, because she is old enough to go along with us now."

"Mother," asked Sandra. "Do I HAVE to go to Sunday School? Do all of you HAVE to go, too?"

"Do you suppose Daddy and I do everything for you because we HAVE to?" said Mother, pouring the juice.

"Well, I guess it's because you love me," said Sandra slowly.

"God loves us so much," explained Daddy, "that we love Him too, and want to show it. We go to His house to learn more about Him and to worship Him."

"We haven't much time left," said Mother. "Do you want me to lay out your blue ruffled dress, Sandra?"

Sandra looked at the family, hurrying to prepare for Sunday School. She looked out the window again at the birds and the garden. She felt sorry that she had pouted. Now she nodded real hard to Mother and ate breakfast.

"Mother, will I have time to pick a few daisies? My Sunday School teacher asked if we would like to bring something to show our love for Jesus. I think daisies would make our church room look pretty and show Jesus I love Him."

Mother smiled. "You may if you hurry. But I'm sure that God will be MOST pleased when you show your love by bringing YOURSELF to His house."

— —LEONA CHOY

41

Connie's promise

Connie was up almost as early as the little birds outside her window. She dressed herself and even tied a double knot in her shoestrings. Now that Baby Jack was in their family Connie was a BIG sister!

"Good morning, Miss Sunshine!" said Mother as Connie tiptoed into the kitchen. Mother was just putting the milk into a bottle for Baby Jack.

"What a lot of clothes to wash since Baby Jack came last month!" said Connie, looking at the clothes baskets. "I'm going to help you ALL day, Mother," she promised.

"I'm very pleased, Connie. I'm sure that Jesus is also pleased that you want to help."

Ring-Ring went the telephone. Connie ran to answer it before the noise could wake Baby Jack.

"Oh, Mother! It's Aunt Nell! She wants to know if I can go to the country with her today." Connie's eyes sparkled as she waited for Mother to give her permission.

Suddenly she thought of her promise to help Mother.

"Do whatever you think you should," said Mother, beginning to gather up the clothes for the washing.

Connie could almost see the friendly farm with the chickens, cows, and the new kittens Aunt Nell told about. She turned slowly back to the telephone.

"I'm sorry, Aunt Nell, but I am going to help Mother today."

As the morning went on, Connie found out how much fun it really was to help Mother with everything.

"Can you be my table, Connie?" said Mother as the clothes were ready to hang on the line.

"But how can I?" Connie looked puzzled.

"Just put both arms out straight and I'll put the box of clothespins on them and you'll be my table!"

Connie laughed. "This is fun!" she said, as she followed Mother around between the clotheslines.

"Now be my vacuum cleaner," said Mother, inside the house again. "Go around all the rooms and pick up the papers and other things that are out of place."

Buzzz! Here I come," said Connie, going into the corners and under the chairs and tables.

"Now, for a treat, you may be my chair," said Mother, bringing Baby Jack down from his room.

"But how?" questioned Connie, her eyes wide with surprise.

"Sit right there, feet on the floor and your back straight like a chair. Now you may hold Baby Jack and feed him his bottle. Today you have shown what a grown-up girl you are becoming."

Connie carefully held Baby Jack and felt his warm little hand. She was not sorry that she had obeyed the voice of the Lord and kept her promise to help Mother. She felt GLAD!

— —LEONA CHOY

"Obey the voice of the Lord"
—Jeremiah 26:13.

Two pennies for Nancy

"Thank you, Mrs. Jackson," said Nancy as her feet hopped down the steps.

Mrs. Jackson was an old lady who lived a few houses away from Nancy. Every day Nancy would run to the corner drugstore for Mrs. Jackson to pick up the daily paper. She almost always gave Nancy a penny for running the errand. Today was a special day, for as Nancy hopped down the steps, she had more than one penny. Mrs. Jackson had given her two pennies!

Nancy's mother always let her buy candy with the money, but made her promise not to buy it until after supper, for she did not want it to spoil her appetite. Nancy always kept her promise.

But today she had two cents. Mother would never know it if she disobeyed and spent one for candy *now*. She could save one for after supper.

As she walked along, she saw Timmy sucking on a big lollipop. "Hi, Timmy," she said. As she looked closer, she saw it was orange, her favorite flavor. "Where did you get your lollipop?"

"Just around the corner in the new candy store," said Timmy.

Oh, Nancy wanted a lollipop very much. But she knew she would be disobeying her mother if she got it before supper. She knew the Lord wouldn't be pleased either. Her feet stopped. Both feet seemed to turn her around right toward the store. Nancy needed help.

"Help me, Lord, to do right," she prayed. Then she carefully turned her feet around again, so they pointed right toward home.

On her way she saw some boys and girls playing. They were making believe they were on a lion hunt. A few of the boys were the lions, and most of the girls were chasing them. Nancy's feet were soon running after the lions as fast as they could.

"Nancy, time for supper," Mother's voice called.

All during supper, she wanted to tell Mommy and Daddy about the two pennies, but she kept it a big secret instead. She was planning something special.

After supper she helped her mother with the dishes. Then her feet skipped around the corner to the new candy store where Timmy had said he bought his lollipop. She told the man she had two cents and wanted to buy something for three people!

With six gumdrops in a sack she ran home to surprise Mommy and Daddy. They were pleased with her treat.

When Nancy prayed that night, she thanked God for helping her feet to obey. She was glad that she had not disappointed Mommy and Daddy, but she was even more glad that she had not disappointed Jesus.

———Winifred Nielsen

"Children, obey your parents"
—Ephesians 6:1.

43

First day at school

Tommy zipped up his jacket and got in line with the rest of the children. Kindergarten was such fun! He was to go every afternoon at the same time that his big brother Max went. Today Tommy and Max had gone hand in hand down the sidewalk. They had waited for the patrol boy to tell them when to cross the street. And then they were at the school.

"Now be SURE to wait at the side gate for Max to come and get you after school," Mother had said. "Never leave the gate."

The bell rang and all the children marched out to the yard where mothers, brothers, and sisters were waiting. Tommy stood by the gate. He waited and waited. Nearly everyone had gone. Even Sally who lived next door had gone home with her big sister. But Max didn't come after him.

Tommy looked through the gate down the street to his own house. He could almost see his front porch.

And then he saw Max already at home, playing on his scooter with another boy. How surprised Tommy was! Max had forgotten him! Would Max come back? Tommy thought and thought. How was he to get home? Should he try to go home alone?

He started toward the corner. Big trucks zoomed by. Cars honked at each other at the busy corner. The patrol boys had gone home. Tommy was afraid. He didn't know what to do.

But then he knew. "Please, God, help me," he prayed in his heart as he wiped his hot face with his sleeve. Then it seemed that he knew what to do.

"Mother told me NOT to go alone, so I WILL obey her. I'll just wait and God will be with me," he said aloud.

Then he saw somebody running toward the corner across the street. It was Max! Tommy saw Max watch the traffic lights until they changed and then he carefully crossed the street to the school side. He hurried to the side gate with a big grin all over his face.

"Hey, Tom!" he called. "I forgot that I had a brother who is big enough to go to school and I went right home without you! Well, here I am. Mother reminded me." He took Tommy by the hand.

Tommy didn't feel like saying anything much. He just felt very glad. Max took Tommy's hand.

"Mother said she knew you would still be here because you are big enough to go to school, and big enough to obey her," said Max.

Tommy felt wonderful inside. God had helped him be brave because he had obeyed every word Mother had said!

—LEONA CHOY

"Children, obey your parents"
—Ephesians 6:1.

A verse learned twice

Joey's Daddy shut the big Bible and put it back on the shelf.

"I know five verses now," said Joey, drawing himself up tall. "That's a LOT of them!"

Mother smiled as she put the cereal away. "D o y o u want to say that new one again, just to be sure you have it right?"

"Obey the voice of the Lord," said Joey in his loudest, clearest voice.

"Joey! Come on out and play!" called his friend Billy from the door. A tricycle bell rang as if it were in a hurry too.

Joey galloped toward the back door. "Whoa, horsie!" called Daddy. "Didn't you forget something?"

With his hand on the doorknob Joey pouted. "I can't help clear away dishes this morning. I'm in a hurry. Billy is waiting for me to play."

Daddy took the pencil hanging beside a chart on the wall. He erased the check he had just put beside Joey's fifth verse to show that Joey had learned it.

"Don't do that, Daddy! I know my verse real well!"

"Obey the voice of the Lord"
—Jeremiah 26:13.

Joey's lips began to tremble. He walked slowly to the table again.

"I don't think you do," said Mother. "You can say it with your mouth but do you know it in your heart? To KNOW a verse is to DO what it says. Even the parakeet can learn to say words!"

Since Daddy and Mother didn't say anything more, Joey turned and went out the back door.

He took his wagon from the garage and coasted down the driveway. Billy must have gone back to his house without waiting. There was no one else around. Edna must be helping her Mother tend the baby. She wasn't outside to play either. Nearly all the children had jobs to do for their parents.

Joey was lonely. He wondered why he didn't feel right. "Let's see," he thought, "maybe I could practice my verses some more alone."

"Obey the voice . . . ." he began. Then he stopped. Back up the driveway he ran and into the house.

Mother was upstairs sweeping. Daddy had gone to work. He was all alone and the dishes were still on the table. Quickly he took the tray and loaded it with as many as he could carry. It took three trips to get them all piled neatly on the cabinet in the kitchen.

When he finished he noticed his verse chart. He stood on a chair, took the pencil, and put the check beside his new verse again. Then he put ANOTHER big check beside it.

"I learned this one TWICE," Joey laughed. "Once with my mouth and once with my heart!"

——LEONA CHOY

45

Surprise by airmail

Ring-Ring went the doorbell.

Charles ran to answer it. There stood the postman with a strange little box.

"Father, hurry!" shouted Charles as he ran to the basement. "Some funny-looking mail is here!"

Father wiped his hands after greasing the lawn mower. Big Brother Hal ran out of his bedroom, still carrying his model car. They all hurried to the door but Charles got there first.

"Sign here, please," said the postman as he handed Father a pencil and card.

Inside the house the children could hardly keep their hands off the screened wooden box with the little hinged door. Hopping inside—well, you guessed it—was the prettiest blue and green bird you could imagine!

"A parrot!" shouted Charles.

"Don't be silly. That's a parakeet!" said Hal. "I studied about them. Say, he sure is a dandy!"

"It says on the tag, 'To all of you, from Uncle Frank.' Why this bird was sent across the country by airmail!" exclaimed Father.

"What a traveler!" said Hal. "Is he the kind that you can teach to talk and do tricks?"

"That's right," answered Father. "But I'm not so sure that we can keep him."

"But why?" cried both boys at once.

"Mother has many things to do all day long and she doesn't have any time to take care of him and teach him."

"Oh Father," said Charles, "since he belongs to us all, we all can help."

"Sure," added Hal. "We'll each have certain jobs. We've GOT to keep him!"

Hal ran next door to borrow the neighbor's book about parakeets. In a few minutes a list was made of all the things he would need.

"Cage, bird seed, bird gravel, cuttlebone, bells, toys . . . ." read Father. "Say, that's going to cost a lot."

"Couldn't I let him use the bells I had on my ice skates if we tie them to a string?" asked Hal.

"And couldn't I fix up that plastic ladder from my fire engine on his cage?" asked Charles.

"I've got some money from my paper route," said Hal, "and some birthday money too."

"Well," said Charles slowly, "I got 25 cents from Uncle Carl last week. That's quite a bit, isn't it?"

"Looks like the parakeet will be well taken care of after all," laughed Father. "God is pleased when we share what we have and also share in the work. Maybe we could all build a gym for the bird, from that wood we have in the basement."

Chirp-Cheep, said the little bird, cocking his head as if to say he was happy to be part of this happy family.

— —Leona Choy

"Let us love one another"
—I John 4:7.

46

Double helpers

"Everybody is raking their leaves, Davy," said Danny, his twin brother. "I wonder if they wouldn't like to have us haul away the leaves in our nice new red wagons."

"Let's go ask," said Davy.

Down the street they went, Davy going on the left side and Danny on the right.

Davy stopped at every house along the left side but nobody seemed to want their leaves hauled away. Only one house was left on his side of the street and that was Mrs. Horn's. Davy had never been to her house. People said Mrs. Horn was very old and didn't have much money.

Davy almost turned back when he heard the *scritch-scritch* of a rake. He grew bolder and turned up Mrs. Horn's driveway, pulling his wagon.

"Pardon me," said Davy, "but would you like to have your leaves taken away?"

The little old lady turned slowly around and leaned on her rake. She smiled such a friendly smile that Davy was really glad he came.

"God bless you, young man! But I've been sick and I don't think I'm even strong enough to finish this raking!" she said kindly.

"Oh, I'm very strong," said Davy proudly. "Let me rake your lawn."

"But I won't be able to give you any money for your help," said Mrs. Horn shaking her head sadly.

"Aw, that's all right," replied Davy. "I learned in Sunday School that we are to do things just to please God anyway."

Mrs. Horn went into the house and Davy started to work on the lawn. It was hard work.

Soon he heard the rattle of another wagon and Danny came around the hedge.

"Hey, what are you doing here? How much money are you getting for this?"

"I'm doing this for Jesus," stated Davy with importance. "Mrs. Horn says she hasn't any money to give but she's too weak to do it herself so I'm doing it for her," said Davy all in one breath.

"Boy, that's something. I got two nickels for hauling two loads. If I share one of them with you, will you let me help you with this lawn? I want to do something for Jesus too!"

A short while later Mrs. Horn came out with a plate of still-warm cookies. She laughed in surprise when she saw two boys, looking just alike, with two red wagons, just alike, working on her lawn!

After they ate lots of cookies, Davy and Danny pulled their wagons home.

"Davy," said Danny, "I feel even better doing that work for Jesus than I did getting paid for the other work. Even if we hadn't gotten cookies!"

"Let us love one another"
—I John 4:7.

———LEONA CHOY

Tony gets even

"You just wait!" shouted Tony. "I'll do something to you next time and I'll make it bad, *bad*, BAD!" Everything inside Tony just felt like bursting.

"Aw, you're just a sissy, Tony," called Dennis. "You can't take a little joke!" He rode off down the sidewalk on his bike.

Tony ran up his porch steps and into the house. "Daddy!" he cried.

"In here, Tony," answered Daddy from his workshop.

Tony rubbed his eyes with his sleeve when he came in. Daddy shut off his buzz saw and sat down on the bench.

"Something wrong, Tony?"

"Dennis is a mean boy!" said Tony stamping his foot. "I don't like him and I'm going to hurt him good when I get a chance."

"Tony, do you think it pleases Jesus for you to talk like that?"

"But he took my cowboy rope and tied all the wheels of my tricycle up so I can't even ride it!" Tony just had to let a few tears roll out of his eyes.

"Well, Son, perhaps he was just having a little fun and didn't mean any harm. Anyway, we can fix the trike up so you can ride it again." Daddy began to sweep up the sawdust. "And would it really do you any good to hurt Dennis?"

"It would pay him back," said Tony.

"Yes, but then he'd have to pay YOU back again and you'd be fighting all the time," said Daddy.

"Is there any way you can get even with him that's better?" asked Daddy with a secret smile.

Tony thought a moment. "Just hurt him MOST, then he won't do it any more."

"Would Jesus like to have you do it that way?" questioned Daddy.

"No, I suppose not. Our Sunday School teacher said God wants us to forgive each other."

"And love one another, too," added Daddy. "If you do something good to Dennis, he won't have to pay you back with something bad."

While Tony was thinking this over, Daddy started to put the pieces of something together that he had been making.

"Daddy, what is it?" asked Tony. "Is it—my boat?"

"Sure is. I've just finished it and thought you might like to drive over to the lake and try sailing it now."

"And would you like a little lunch packed up for you two sailors to take along?" asked Mother, coming into the workshop.

"Oh, that would be fun!" shouted Tony. "And Mother—could you put in an extra sandwich? I think, if you'll let me, I'll ask Dennis if he can come along with us to the lake."

Tony began to feel very happy as he ran outside to find Dennis. He knew this would please God more than thinking up something bad to do to Dennis.

——LEONA CHOY

"Let us love one another"
—I John 4:7.

Missionary picnic

"A picnic!" shouted Alice.

"Lots of food and fun!" echoed Howard, her brother, jumping up and down.

"Is everyone going to bring something?" Howard asked Mother, as she packed a big basket with good things.

"No, our family is bringing everything this time, children. These other people are the missionaries from our church that you have been praying for. They have been living far away in South America and we want to give them a nice time while they are here," Mother explained.

"Are they the family we send our Sunday School money to, so that they can tell the people about Jesus?" asked Alice.

"Yes, they are. Sally and Roy are just about your ages too."

"Did they go to school in South America? Do they speak a different language?" asked Howard.

"They had to go to a special school there with the children of other missionaries. Maybe you can ask them today if they can teach you some words in another language," said Mother.

"What fun! Maybe they can write some letters to us after they go back.

We could get some South American postage stamps!" said Alice, helping Mother butter the sandwiches.

"They are going to travel for a few months in their car to many cities, telling people in different churches about their work," explained Mother.

"Boy, that might be fun for a while. But they won't have much to do, riding in a car all the time," said Howard. "Do you suppose they have anything to read or play with?"

"I imagine they had to leave most of their toys in South America. They flew here by airplane."

"I'm glad we have lots of toys," said Howard. "Can we have some peanut butter sandwiches too? I think the missionary children will like them."

"Mother," said Alice, who had been thinking very hard, "I would like to give Sally my book of games."

"To keep?" asked Howard. "The one you got for your birthday?"

"Sure, Howard. I have lots of books. That's my favorite, but maybe it would be her favorite too."

"Well—I wonder if Roy might like my set of Bible puzzles. He could work those in the car. It's my BEST set!" said Howard proudly.

"This is more fun than keeping everything for ourselves, isn't it, Howard?" said Alice, clapping her hands.

"It makes me feel good too," said Howard. "Jesus is pleased when we share."

"Especially when you share the BEST that you have, children," said Mother, as she gave them chocolate cookies.

— —LEONA CHOY

"Let us love one another"
—I John 4:7.

Second pair of hands

"Guess what happened, Mommy!" shouted Cliff as he ran into the kitchen, puffing to catch his breath. "Guess what happened!"

"I can't imagine," said Mommy as she swept away the crumbs from the table.

"Mr. Johnson broke his leg!"

There, it was out! The biggest news Cliff had had to tell for a long time.

"Oh, dear! How?" asked Mommy.

"I think he fell from the ladder when he was painting," answered Cliff.

"What a pity!" said Mommy. "We'll all have to pitch in and help them. I'll go next door and see how things are."

"They have gone to the hospital and will be back at lunch time," reported Mommy. "I shall make a hot dish for them to eat when they get back."

"I will go and mow the lawn for Mr. Johnson," said Daddy.

"And I will go over and do their dusting," said Janet, who was ten.

Mommy began to peel potatoes for the hot dish when she noticed Cliff standing silently by her side.

"But what can I do? I want to help."

"You're too little to help," teased

"Let us love one another"
—I John 4:7.

Janet, skipping out the door.

"No, you aren't," said Mommy. "I'll give you a very important job."

Cliff brightened up.

"Please watch Gary in the play pen. He doesn't want to stay alone."

"But that isn't exciting. That isn't helping the Johnsons any," pouted Cliff.

"Oh, but it is. If I'd have to watch him myself, I couldn't do the things we want to for the Johnsons."

"All right. I'll do it," said Cliff. He took his pail and shovel and went out to play in the sandpile near Gary's play pen. Gary jabbered as he played happily, now that someone was near.

Buzz-buzz went the lawn mower.

Clatter-bang went the dishes in the kitchen. Soon Cliff smelled baking cake. How hungry he was!

Then Cliff heard the slam of a car door. The Johnsons were home. He ran in to tell Mommy. She was just scraping the last of the frosting from the bowl and gave the spoon to Cliff to lick.

"You have been a real helper this morning. You are Mommy's second pair of hands!" she said with a laugh. "I'm going to let you take these things next door in the basket."

"All by myself? That's a big job!"

"But you have shown that you know how to please God. You do well whatever you can to help others," said Mommy.

It was all Cliff could do to keep from skipping with happiness all the way over to the Johnsons. He had done something important after all. He had been Mommy's second pair of hands!

——Leona Choy

Georgie's uncle's wheelchair

Though Georgie's Uncle John could not walk, he could do many wonderful things. He sat in his wheelchair while he made tables, cabinets, wooden toys, and all kinds of valuable wooden things for people who helped to take care of him.

Usually, Georgie's bigger brothers and sisters would take turns pushing Uncle John in his wheelchair around the house or to the hardware store or wherever he wanted to go. Georgie wanted to help, too, but when he tried they would say, "You're just in the way, Georgie. Let *us* do it! Uncle John's wheelchair is too heavy for you."

That made Georgie feel sad. He knew a Bible verse by heart: *Let us do good unto all*. He wanted to do good to Uncle John, too, didn't he?

One day Georgie's bigger brothers and sisters were all in school when Uncle John found that he needed some brass handles to complete a cupboard he was building for Mother.

Uncle John said, "I wish the boys would come home from school. I need a push to the hardware store."

"I'll push you," said Georgie.

"This is a heavy wheelchair," said Uncle John, "and it's almost a block to the hardware store."

"I can try, can't I?" asked Georgie.

Uncle John was willing to let him try, so Mother helped to get the wheelchair out to the sidewalk. Then Mother and Georgie helped Uncle John into the wheelchair. Georgie went behind it. He put his hands on the handle and pushed with all his might.

"Is it too heavy, Georgie?" asked Uncle John. "Is it too hard for you?"

Just then the wheelchair began to move. "I'm pushing it, Uncle John!" Georgie shouted happily. "I'm pushing it all by myself!"

Of course Georgie could not push very fast, and the trip took a long time. Uncle John purchased a bag of gleaming brass handles at the hardware store. Then he and Georgie had an ice cream cone from the drugstore before they started back.

When Georgie's brothers and sisters came home from school, they saw Uncle John screwing the handles on the beautiful new cupboard. "How did you get to the hardware store?" they asked.

Uncle John smiled. "I didn't have to wait for anyone to come home from school because Georgie pushed me!"

"How could you do it?" they asked Georgie, surprised.

Georgie felt very happy. "I wanted to please Jesus by doing good to Uncle John," he said. "So I tried very hard, and I did it!"

—— Wanda Schickling

"Let us love one another"
—I John 4:7.

51

Neighbors

The doctor looked at the thermometer. Then he looked at the red spots on Russell.

"No doubt about it. This young man has measles!"

Russell didn't feel well. It didn't matter that he'd have to stay in bed. He only wanted to sleep.

After a few days he felt better. "Look, Mother. Those red spots are going away. I'm well now."

"Not quite well yet," said Mother. "You'll have to stay indoors for quite a few days yet. But I have a surprise for you. While you were sick, Aunt June brought you some toys, Uncle Bill sent you three new books, and your Sunday School teacher sent you a Bible game and a color book. You will have lots to keep you busy!"

What fun Russell had with these new toys! It was fun to play with the older toys he loved so well, too.

"Guess what!" said Mother that night. "The new boy who just moved in next door has the measles too! His name is George."

"Well," said Russell, "I think he is having as much fun as I am. I don't mind being indoors at all."

"George's mother has to work all day.

He has to stay alone with his older sister. He doesn't have a Daddy," explained his mother. "I don't think that George has very much to do. I didn't see any toys around when I went over there today."

"No toys?" wondered Russell as he looked around his room at all the toys and books that lined his shelves and bookcase. "Do you suppose he could come over and play with mine?"

"I don't think so. He isn't well enough yet," answered Mother as she brought Russell a glass of cold milk and a sugar cooky.

"Mother, do you think it would please Jesus if I would share some of my things with George? I could even wrap them up like presents."

Russell put his slippers on and got out of bed. He picked out one after another of his books and toys until he had a little box full.

"I'll bring you some wrapping paper and string, Russell," said Mother. "And also some pretty seals to put on the paper."

"I'm going to send my Sunday School papers from last week too. Do you suppose that George goes to Sunday School?"

"I don't think so, Son. His family just moved here. Perhaps he would go with you when you both get well. You can show him right now that you love Jesus and love him too by sharing what you have with him."

"It's more fun," said Russell, "to give these things away than it was to get them!"

— —Leona Choy

"Let us love one another"
—I John 4:7.

The Best Builder

Glenn ran down the street. Eddie and Roy were already sitting on the pile of boards stacked near the sidewalk. Glenn scrambled up beside Roy. This was a splendid place to watch the building of the new house.

"See?" Eddie pointed at one of the workmen. "That's my father. I told you he was going to build this house."

The boys watched Eddie's father carry long boards and nail them into place. "*Nobody* could make anything better than a house!" Eddie said proudly.

"My father makes airplanes," Roy said. "Nobody could make anything that goes higher than an airplane. What does your father make, Glenn?"

"He—doesn't make things," Glenn said. "He works in an office."

The other boys looked at him without speaking. Then they talked about houses and airplanes.

After a while Glenn slid down and said, "I think I'll go home."

He walked slowly homeward, wishing that *he* knew someone who could make wonderful things.

That night he went to bed, as he always did, before it was quite dark. Later he awakened, not to a bright new day but in a dark, dark room. He had always wanted to know what the night looked like, so he slipped out of bed and ran to the window. The trees were like enormous black giants. As he stared at them they seemed to come closer. A gust of wind moved their branches like great arms reaching out to him. Without meaning to, Glenn cried out, "Father!"

Then slowly he looked up, up, up, to see how big these giants were. And suddenly, high above them he saw the sky, dotted with hundreds of stars twinkling like tiny lanterns.

His father came into the room and asked, "What's the matter, Glenn?"

"I was scared—for a minute," Glenn said. "The trees looked like giants."

"But now the moon is coming up," Father said, "and you can see they are just our friendly trees."

Glenn nodded. He didn't speak for a while. Then he said, "Eddie's father builds houses and Roy's father makes airplanes. But they couldn't make the things my heavenly Father has made, could they? *Nobody* could make a moon or a star or a tree. Nobody but God!"

The next day Glenn sat with his friends on the pile of boards.

"I know Somebody who makes something better than a house and higher than airplanes," he said to his friends.

"Who?" they both asked in surprise.

"My heavenly Father," answered Glenn. "He made the trees for the houses, and the stars and moon 'way up in the sky."

— —Aileene Sargent

"All things were made by Him"
—John 1:3.

53

Dorie's gray day

It all began when Dorie wanted—of all things —*strawberry soda* for breakfast! She wouldn't d r i n k milk and said she *hated* water.

"Oh-oh," s a i d Caroline. "This is going to be one of Dorie's gray days."

"Dear, dear," said Gramps. "I was hoping it would be a sunny day."

Now Dorie's gray days and sunny days had nothing whatever to do with the weather. Sometimes when it was raining hard, Dorie was as sunny as could be. But today, although sunbeams came dancing through the window, Dorie was having a gray day.

"I thought we might ride out to the country," Gramps went on. "But if this is going to be a gray day—"

"Oh, it won't be," Dorie promised.

So they got into Gramps' old car and away they went. He found a bag of peanuts in his pocket. Soon the bag was empty! And the girls were thirsty.

They turned off the main highway onto a quiet country road and drove along looking at the leaves that had been touched by frost in the night and turned to bronze and red and gold.

Suddenly the car made a strange noise and jerked to a stop. Gramps could not get it started again and there they were, far from the main highway and not a house in sight. Gramps had forgotten to put water in the radiator!

"It's too far to walk back to the highway," he said. "We'll just have to wait until another car comes along."

"I'm thirsty," Caroline complained.

Dorie was thirsty, too. But she was ashamed to say so, since she had refused to drink anything that morning.

They grew tired of waiting. It seemed no other cars were traveling this lonely road. Dorie's throat felt hot and dry. She didn't care if she never tasted strawberry soda again. All she wanted was a drink of water.

Gramps let them get out of the car and run around. As they played, Dorie parted some bushes, to hide from Caroline. She gave a cry of delight.

"Gramps!" she called. "Look!"

Gramps and Caroline came quickly. A tiny stream gurgled and rushed along on its way to the far-off river.

"How shall we drink it?" Caroline asked. "Like puppies?"

But Gramps said, "You mustn't drink it at all. It's all right for the thirsty car, but you will have to wait until we get home."

Finally Gramps got the old car started and they drove straight home.

The first thing they did was to get glasses of water. Dorie held hers for a moment. "Gramps," she said. "Whatever would we do if we didn't have any water at all?" She took a long cool drink. Then she whispered, "Thank You, God, for giving us water."

Gramps smiled. He was glad Dorie's day had not been gray after all.

— —AILEENE SARGENT

"All things were made by Him"
—John 1:3.

54

Amy's search

The toy teapot was filled with chocolate milk. The tiny sandwiches were just the right size for the play dishes. When Amy had poured chocolate milk into the little cups, she passed the sandwiches to Lela, her new friend. But Lela folded her hands and bowed her head.

"Is—something wrong?" Amy asked.

"Why, no," Lela said, smiling. "I was waiting for you to say grace."

Amy looked puzzled.

"Grace," Lela repeated. "You know —thanking God for the food."

"Oh, that's all right." Amy laughed. *"Mother* gave us the food."

But Lela shook her head. " 'All things were made by *Him,' "* she said.

"I know one thing He didn't make," Amy said. "Bread! My mother made it."

Again Lela shook her head. And closing her eyes, she prayed softly, "Thank You, God, for giving us this food."

Amy was quiet. But after Lela went home she asked, "Mother, where did you get the flour to make the bread?"

"From the food store," Mother said.

Amy went to the food store. "Mr. Hanson," she asked, "where did you get the flour you sold to Mother?"

"All things were made by Him"
—John 1:3.

"Direct from the flour mill," he said.

At dinnertime Amy begged, "Father, tell me about the flour mill."

Father didn't know much about flour mills. But he promised to take Amy to see one the next Saturday.

It was a long drive. But they finally came to a huge flour mill. There a man showed them how *wheat* is cleaned and ground and sifted until it becomes fine white flour.

"Where do you get the wheat?" Amy wanted to know.

"From the farmers," said the man.

On the way home they saw a farmer working in a field. Father stopped the car so Amy could ask him about wheat.

"We have some in the barn," the farmer said. "Come and see."

He put some grains of wheat into Amy's hand and said, "We saved this for seed to plant the field again."

"But where did the *first seed* come from?" Amy whispered in awe.

"In the beginning," the farmer explained, "when God created the earth, He said, 'Let the earth bring forth grass . . . and fruit . . . *whose seed is in itself.'* Wheat is one of the grasses He made. And wheat makes its own seed, as God said it should."

When Amy got home she ran over to Lela's house. "I was wrong, Lela," she said. "Mother does bake our bread, but she couldn't make it without flour. Flour is made from wheat. And wheat grows from seed that God put in the earth a long long time ago!" Then she bowed her head and said, "Thank You, God, for giving us bread."

— —AILEENE SARGENT

55

The exchange

Ronnie was sulking. He felt angry at his family. So he took his favorite picture puzzle and went over to Alan's house. Alan was sulking, too.

"I brought my puzzle," Ronnie said. "It makes a picture of a family."

They sat on the floor and fitted the pieces together. There was the picture of a family: father, mother, sister. But there was an empty space, for one piece of the puzzle was missing.

"It's a boy," Ronnie said. "Like us."

"Can't find him," Alan said, shaking the box upside down.

Ronnie sighed. "Wish I had a different family. My family are always telling me to *do* things, like picking up my toys and washing my hands."

"*My* family," Alan complained, "are always telling me *not to do* things, like when I climb."

"Why, then," Ronnie said, laughing, "you ought to live at my house and I ought to live at yours! Do you suppose our mothers would let us?"

"Let's ask!" Alan said, jumping up.

They ran to Alan's mother and told her they would like to exchange families. To their surprise, she agreed. Then they ran to Ronnie's house and Ronnie's mother agreed with the boys, too.

So Ronnie went to live at Alan's house and Alan went to live at Ronnie's house. All went well until dinnertime.

Ronnie didn't know how Alan was getting along but *he* wasn't so happy. When Alan's father accidentally stepped on a toy automobile, Ronnie looked tearfully at the broken pieces. Nobody had *told* him to pick it up. He forgot to wash his hands and was ashamed to let Alan's parents see them. Nobody had *told* him to wash them.

Ronnie remembered the picture puzzle and the boy who had left an empty place in the family. He had left an empty place in his family, too. But no! Alan was there. Would his mother and father love Alan as much as they loved him?

Suddenly he wanted his own family. He snatched up his pajamas. He ran from the house. It was almost dark but he ran on.

He bumped into someone and down they tumbled. Ronnie picked himself up. Alan picked himself up, too. He had a bandage on one knee.

"I skinned my knee at your house!" he told Ronnie, accusingly.

"How?" asked Ronnie.

"We-ell," Alan admitted. "I climbed. But nobody told me *not* to!"

"Huh!" said Ronnie. "I'm going home. I like my own family."

Alan bobbed his head. "So do I."

"I think," Ronnie said slowly, "that God must have put families together the way they *belong*. They just don't *fit* any other way."

——Aileene Sargent

Billy and the snow children

Everybody felt sorry for Billy. His friend Arthur had moved away and he was very lonely. His father gave him new toys, the neighbors waved when they passed, and the big boys who saw Billy playing by himself would call out, "Hi, Billy." But they never stopped to play.

When the snow came, Billy missed Arthur more than ever. One day the big boys came right into Billy's yard and said, "Let's make a snow man, Billy."

"I don't know how," Billy told them.

"We'll help you," they said. So they packed some snow into a ball and rolled it on the ground to make it bigger.

Billy watched for a while. Then he asked, "Could you make snow children instead?"

"Sure," they said. So they made a boy and a girl out of snow. "Now you will have someone to play with," they told Billy, laughing. "Run, ask your mother for some clothes to put on them."

Mother was helpful. She gave them a beanie cap and an old coat of Billy's for the snow boy. An old blouse and an apron made a nice dress for the girl.

"There now," the boys said. "Don't they look real? 'By, Billy. Have fun!"

So Billy was left alone with the snow children. He made believe they were real children who had come to play with him. But he soon forgot it was all make-believe and he talked to the snow children as if they were alive.

"Let's have a snow fight!" he cried, throwing soft snow at them.

But they didn't throw any at him.

"Chase me!" he cried, running as fast as he could around the yard.

But they didn't chase him. So Billy came back. He looked at the snow children and his eyes filled with tears.

"Course you can't run," he said sadly. "Your legs are just made of snow."

He turned away and there were three children watching him from the gate.

"Whom were you talking to?" the boy asked.

"I was talking to the snow children," Billy said. "But they can't talk."

The children came closer. "If they *could* talk, what do you think they would say?" the smallest one asked.

Billy looked at the snow children and now his eyes were filled with laughter. "They'd say, 'You silly Billy! You ought to know that only God can make real live children.'" He turned and smiled at the boy who was just his size, at the girl who was bigger and at the smallest one. "Make-believe is fun," he said. "But I like real live friends best."

And Billy walked away from the snow children with his new friends.

— —Aileene Sargent

"A friend loves at all times"
—Proverbs 17:17.

Hidden power

The wind swept past in a great hurry. It tried to tug Marcia's curls from beneath her hood and nipped Jay's nose till it was red as a cherry.

"Where does the wind come from?" Marcia wondered.

"Where does it go?" Jay asked. He looked down the street. "I'm going to run with the wind and find out where it goes!" And away he raced with the wind at his back.

"I want to know where it comes from," Marcia called. Off she ran with the wind in her face.

At the end of the block a strong gust came around the corner. So Marcia turned the corner and ran on. Where was its hiding place? Where *did* the wind start?

She turned the next corner and there was Jay running toward her! How they laughed! They had run around the block, searching for the wind's home.

"I couldn't find where the wind begins," Marcia said.

"We know it's here." Jay was frowning now. "We can feel it blow. But where does it come from and where does it go?"

"All things were made by Him"
—John 1:3.

Marcia smiled. "God must send it," she said, "to sweep the world clean."

"How?" Jay asked. "If God is way up in heaven and we're down here—"

"I don't know," Marcia said. "I just know He gives us everything we need. So He must make the wind blow, too."

"Huh!" Jay grunted, unbelieving.

They went home together but Marcia was troubled. How could she help Jay understand that God is not far away? That He loves the world He made and, *somehow,* takes care of it?

The smell of fresh cookies drew them to the kitchen. Granny gave them milk and cookies. Then she said, "Will you please turn on the light, Jay?"

The light switch was in the wall near the kitchen door. As Jay reached to touch it, Marcia ran and held his hand.

"How do you know the room will light up if you turn the switch?" she asked.

"It always does," Jay said. "Look!" He moved the switch and the kitchen was flooded with light.

"But *how* can that tiny switch way over here in the wall make that thing in the ceiling light up?" Marcia asked.

"The switch sends 'lectric power to the light in the ceiling," Jay explained. "You can't *see* the *power* but . . ."

"That's the way it is with God's power!" Marcia cried. "We can't *see* it but we *know it's there!* We can *see* the things He has made and we *have* all the good things He has given us!"

"Why, of course!" Jay agreed. "That's how it is. Nobody but God could make the wind blow!"

— —AILEENE SARGENT

The travels of a penny

The first thing Bright New Penny remembered was being rolled up tightly in some paper with a lot of other pennies. This was not very exciting. But he wondered what would happen.

Soon the paper was torn and all the pennies spilled into a cash drawer. This was fun, for every time the drawer was opened the pennies rolled about and one never knew—the other pennies told him—just when one would be taken out and started on a new journey.

One time a large coin was dropped in. *"I'm* a quarter," he boasted. "I'm worth as much as 25 of you pennies."

"It seems to me," Bright New Penny said, "if one penny spends his life well, he can do some good."

Before Quarter could answer, Bright New Penny was taken out and given to a man, who dropped him into his pocket. There he met other coins.

"You *do* look quite worn," he said to Thin Dime.

Thin Dime answered sadly, "Some people spend us so foolishly."

"Yes," said Dull Nickel. "Some people have more than they need and instead of letting us help others, they buy something they don't need at all."

"O give thanks unto the Lord, for He is good" —Psalm 107:1.

"But that is selfish!" cried Bright New Penny. *"I* want to do good!"

Just then he was taken from the pocket and handed to a little boy.

"Here are ten pennies for your Sunday School offering," a deep voice said.

The little boy put the pennies into his pocket and went to Sunday School.

"Ah!" thought Bright New Penny. "Now I shall do something worth while. I shall help to care for God's house."

But when the offering box was passed the little boy dropped the pennies in, one by one, until he came to Bright New Penny. He started to put it back into his pocket, but suddenly it fell and rolled into a dark corner! And there Bright New Penny lay all week long.

Then a man came to sweep the floor. He found Bright New Penny.

On Sunday morning he watched the children come into Sunday School. One little girl paused at the door and looked at a dime in her hand.

"I have one dime," she said to the man, "and I can't decide whether to put it in the offering box or give it to the missionary for Toro."

So the man gave Bright New Penny to the little girl. Now Bright New Penny was anxious indeed! Would the little girl do as the little boy had done?

But when the teacher asked, "Who would like to give something to help Toro?" the little girl was the very first to bring her offering. And she gave it with love. So Bright New Penny glowed more brightly than ever, for he knew that he was really going to do some good in the world.

———Aileene Sargent

Leslie's plan

It was Thanksgiving Day and Leslie felt thankful to God for many things. She counted them on her fingers.

"God made the world," she said, and held up one finger. "He sent the Lord Jesus into the world." Up went another finger. "God made me." Up went her third finger. "Jesus loves me." Up went the next finger. Then the rest of her fingers popped up quickly as she added, "God gave me my home, my parents, my food, my clothes, my friends, and— *the snow,*" she ended, running to the window to watch the first big flakes come drifting down.

Soon Leslie was snugly buttoned into her new coat, so thick and warm, with its matching hood and leggings.

As she went outdoors she saw their neighbor go stamping up his front walk.

"Oh, Mr. Kane," she cried, running over to him. "Don't you love the snow?"

"No," said Mr. Kane crossly. "I don't like it. It's cold and wet." And he brushed the snow from his shoulders.

Leslie caught his arm. "Look!" she said. "Look at the snowflake on your sleeve!"

Mr. Kane looked at the snowflake that lay in a lovely lacy pattern on the dark sleeve of his coat.

He smiled. "I never noticed it before," he said. "But snow is really beautiful." And he went into his house.

Leslie turned away and saw her friend, Myra, watching some sparrows.

"Poor little birds," Myra said, as Leslie joined her. "They can't find anything to eat."

"We have more food than we need," Leslie said. "Let's get some bread for the birds."

They went into Leslie's house and got some bread. Then they scattered the crumbs on the ground and watched the hungry birds come fluttering down to eat it up.

Suddenly Myra shivered. "I'm cold," she said.

"*I'm* not cold," Leslie answered.

"That's because you have a nice warm coat," Myra told her.

Then Leslie saw that Myra's coat was thin and shabby.

A little later a thoughtful Leslie walked into her own house. "Mother," she said, "God has given me so much. Would He think me *un*-thankful if I give some away?"

"One of the best ways to show our thankfulness," Mother said, "is to *share* the good things He has given us with those who need them."

"Oh," Leslie cried. "Then there are ever so many things I must do! I'd like to give one of my warm coats to Myra. And I will feed the birds every day. And I think," then her joy spilled out in laughter, "I *think* I shall have to keep on reminding Mr. Kane that God made the beautiful snow."

— —AILEENE SARGENT

"O give thanks unto the Lord, for He is good" —Psalm 107:1.

The shoe bank

The shoe bank stood on a table in Sunday School. Walter watched the other children drop money into it. When it was full it would be sent to a missionary in a far-off land to buy shoes for children in the mission Sunday School.

But the shoe bank had given Walter an idea. *He* would have a shoe bank of his own! Why should he give his money to buy shoes for some other child? His own shoes were scuffed and worn and he did so want a shiny new pair! So whenever he was given money to put in the shoe bank in Sunday School, he took it home and put it in his own shoe bank.

He didn't know how long it would take to save enough for a pair of shoes. But he watched carefully as the coins rattled into the bank.

One day the teacher showed them some pictures the missionary had sent. There was one picture of a boy who looked very cold. Walter wanted to

laugh, for the boy was huddled in a coat that reached from his neck nearly to his feet. Whose coat was he wearing?

But Walter stopped the laugh before it reached his lips. He walked close to the picture and stared. There was snow on the ground and the boy's bare feet were wrapped in rags!

Pointing at them, Walter looked up at the teacher with wide eyes. "Doesn't he have *any shoes at all?*" he asked.

"No shoes at all," she answered.

Walter hung his head. He saw his own shoes and they looked sturdy and good. He began to feel thankful.

All that next week Walter thought about the boy in the picture and other children who had no shoes at all. And each night he whispered "Thank You" to God for his shoes.

Strangely, the more grateful he felt, the less it seemed to matter about having *new* shoes for himself. All he wanted was for the boy in the picture to have shoes as good and warm as his own.

When Sunday came again, Walter opened his shoe bank and took out all the nickels and dimes and pennies and even the two quarters he had put into it. He carried them to Sunday School and dropped them into the shoe bank.

No one knew what Walter had done, but he knew Jesus knew. So he knelt and told the Lord he was sorry that he had almost kept the money for himself.

After that, everytime Walter looked at his shoes, even though they were worn, he was glad he had helped to buy shoes for the children in that far-off land, who didn't have any at all.

——Aileene Sargent

"O give thanks unto the Lord, for He is good" —Psalm 107:1.

Petey's party

All of Petey's friends had been invited to his birthday party. That is, all except one. Petey had not yet asked Bart. The children had been talking about the party for days and Petey knew they would bring him gifts. He wasn't sure about Bart. Maybe Bart didn't have any gift for him. Suddenly Petey felt a mean wish to hurt Bart. He wouldn't invite him to the party. *That* would make Bart feel bad enough.

The day of the party arrived. And inside Petey's home there was such fun and frolic, games and balloons and paper hats! Nobody but Petey saw the lonely little boy who stood outside watching through the window.

All at once, everyone stopped playing and everything was very quiet. The children stood smiling at Petey.

"Just think!" Ralph said. "If Petey had never been born, we wouldn't be having this nice time. 'Cause Petey wouldn't have any birthday!"

How Petey laughed at that! It was good to have a birthday, for that was the time when all your friends were especially loving and kind.

Then he heard Margery say, "Just think! If Jesus had never come to earth, we wouldn't have Christmas either, for that is His birthday!"

No Christmas. What an awful thought! The smile left Petey's face. Christmas, he thought, is the time when all *Jesus'* friends are especially loving and kind to one another. Petey had tried all year to please Him. But what had he done today?

The children were startled when Petey turned, without saying a word, and rushed from the room.

Bart was still standing in front of the house when Petey ran out.

"Bart!" he called. "Come to my party!"

But Bart didn't answer.

"I'm sorry I didn't ask you before," Petey said. "I want you, Bart. I *do.*"

Bart drew his sleeve across his tear-filled eyes and murmured, "But I haven't any gift."

"That doesn't matter," Petey said. "We celebrate Jesus' birthday on Christmas but we don't give Him gifts—I mean *things.* He wants us to *love* Him. And—and to love one another."

Then Bart smiled. And holding hands they ran back into the house.

Now Petey tried hard to make up for his unkindness to his friend. He let Bart choose the next game. Bart sat next to him at the table. And it turned out to be the nicest party Petey could remember.

Afterward Petey looked at his gifts. It didn't matter that Bart had not brought a gift wrapped in paper like the others. Bart was his friend again. And Bart had given him *love.*

— —AILEENE SARGENT

"Call His name Jesus, for He shall save His people from their sins" —Matthew 1:21.

62

Virginia's loving gift

Virginia clasped her hands together tightly to keep from jumping up and down with excitement. When *would* they give out the gifts? It was hard to wait, for she knew she was going to get something she had wanted for so long.

The kindergarten room was gaily decorated. A tree stood in one corner and for weeks the children had been making red and green paper chains and silvery bells. Big bells, little bells, and middle-sized bells they had made by pressing foil over drinking cups, then spreading the edges like the bottoms of real bells.

What a Christmas party! Parents had been invited. There was ice cream and cake and, of course, boxes of Christmas candy heaped under the tree.

Virginia didn't know that the mothers and fathers had been told they might bring a gift to place under the tree. But when she saw the long box Mother tried to hide as they went to the party, she guessed it must hold the gift she wanted above all others—a baby doll!

At last the program was over. As each child's name was called, he or she hurried forward to receive a box of candy and a gift.

Once there was a long pause. Something seemed to have gone wrong. But after a few anxious moments, Virginia's name was called.

She held out her arms to receive the precious box that held the baby doll. But instead she was given a very flat package! She stood quite still, staring at it. The other children were coming forward so she had to move away. Slowly she walked back to her seat and tore the paper from her gift. It was a book of paper dolls. She looked around to find Mother. Then she saw Hester opening the long box. Hester cried out with delight and hugged the baby doll close. Hester didn't have many toys.

Soon the party was over. As Virginia reached her mother's side, she heard the teacher explaining how the tags had come off a couple of the gifts.

"We thought we put them back on the right packages," she said. "I'm so sorry. Come, Virginia. We will take the paper dolls to Hester and tell her the baby doll is yours."

Virginia took the teacher's hand. Then she drew back. She remembered in time how much God loved her and all the children in the world. *He* gave His *only Son.*

Virginia saw Hester still cuddling the baby doll. Then Virginia looked up and smiled through her tears. "It would hurt Hester if we took the doll away," she said. "I want her to keep it."

— —Aileene Sargent

"Call His name Jesus, for He shall save His people from their sins" —Matthew 1:21.

Ready for Christmas

It was the day before Christmas. But everybody in Lucy's house was cross. Mother was cross in the kitchen because the turkey was too big for the roasting pan. Father was cross in the living room because he hurt his hand while setting up the tree. Cliff and Edna quarreled over the gift wrappings.

"Do keep out of my way, Lucy," Mother said.

So Lucy went into the living room. "Stay away from the ladder, Lucy," Father warned.

Then she offered to help wrap gifts. But Cliff said, "Go play someplace else."

Finally Lucy put on her coat and cap and boots and went outdoors. She came to the Widow Joy's cottage.

When Lucy rang the bell Amy Joy came to the door and said, "We're getting ready for Christmas. Come in."

Later, when Lucy went home, Mother asked, "Where have you been, Lucy?"

"Over at the Joys' house," Lucy said. "Getting ready for Christmas."

"That was nice," Mother said. "Did you help to trim their tree?"

Lucy shook her head. "They haven't any tree."

"Maybe she helped to stuff their turkey," Cliff teased.

"They haven't any turkey, either," Lucy said.

"Then what did you do?" Edna asked.

"The Joys were getting their *hearts* ready for Christmas," Lucy explained. "Hugh read the story about Jesus. And we sang about Jesus, too. Then we played a Christmas game. Mrs. Joy said, 'I made a Christmas pudding and I flavored it with something special.' Then we tried to guess what it was."

"What was it?" Cliff asked.

"Gladness!" Lucy told them.

Father snapped his fingers. "I *knew* there was something we forgot," he said. "We forgot to make *our* hearts ready for Christmas. Mother, find out—"

"Yes," said Mother. "I'll find out if the Joys will come over and help us to eat that big turkey."

Cliff and Edna were already sorting packages and changing tags. There must be gifts for their friends, the Joys.

Then Father brought his Bible.

On Christmas morning Mother sang in the kitchen. Father whistled. And laughing voices rang like bells when the Joys arrived!

Lucy was glad they had remembered in time to make their hearts ready for the Lord Jesus' birthday.

——AILEENE SARGENT

"Call His name Jesus, for He shall save His people from their sins" —Matthew 1:21.

64

Little ones, too

It was three days since John and his family moved into the new house. These were happy days for John, for he made many new friends.

But on Sunday morning, when he went out to play, there wasn't another child to be seen. So John walked around the corner and up the street to watch the people going into the church. He wished he could go, too. He decided to tell his family about this church near their new home.

Sure enough! Mother said they would go next Sunday. John was very glad.

Then Aunt Jess spoke, "You aren't going to take John, are you?"

"Yes," Mother said. "Why not?"

"He's too small," Aunt Jess said. "He couldn't sit still."

Too small to go to church! Was God's house only for big people?

"When will I be big enough?" he asked.

Mother smiled. "You may go with us on Sunday," she said.

And John was happy once more.

On Sunday Father and Mother and John walked up the steps of the church and through the great doors.

God's house was not like any other house John had ever seen. It was very quiet—but a comfortable sort of quiet. And all the people had a waiting look as if something nice were going to happen. Then the organ began to play. The music seemed to be all around him and to rise up, up to the high ceiling. He felt sure it was being played to God. He wondered if the tall roof reached up to heaven.

They stood up to sing and bowed to pray. And John was careful not to scuffle his feet or make any noise.

He looked down at his hands. A patch of gold light lay on them. He looked to see where it was coming from, and that was when he discovered the picture-window. It was all colored glass and the sun made it glow as if the people in it were alive. There was Jesus, *blessing* the children after some grownups had tried to send them away. John looked again at the patch of gold light on his hands and he felt as if Jesus were blessing him, too.

Too small to go to church? Why! John thought, God *wants* little children to come to His House so He can bless them.

As they walked home, John saw his playmates and told them happily, "I went to church."

"We went to Sunday School," they said.

"That," Mother explained, "is church for little people, and big people too."

"Oh, Mother!" John said. "I would love to go!"

"So you shall," Mother promised. "Every Sunday."

— —AILEENE SARGENT

"Call His name Jesus, for He shall save His people from their sins" —Matthew 1:21.

Debby's promise

There was a new panda at the zoo and Uncle Ross was coming to take Debby and Jay to see it. And so when Uncle Ross arrived Debby ran to meet him at the door.

"Uncle Ross!" she cried. "Lynn and Norman are going with us! They're our friends and they want to see the panda, too."

But Uncle Ross shook his head. "I couldn't take care of *four* children. It's a nice day and there is sure to be a crowd at the zoo. I might lose a child or two and then what would I do?"

"But I'm a big girl," Debby said, standing as tall as she could. "I'd help you take care of the others. Please, Uncle Ross!"

"We-ell, all right," Uncle Ross finally agreed. "Stay close to me."

There weren't many people watching the polar bears. There weren't many people in the birdhouse. But there was a great crowd near the panda's cage.

Jay dropped his cap. Uncle Ross stooped to pick it up. The crowd pressed forward, and more quickly than you could say 'Jack Robinson,' Uncle Ross and the children were separated!

People were standing so close together the children couldn't see between them, and they were so tall that the children couldn't see over their heads. They couldn't see Uncle Ross at all. But they clung together and pushed to the outer rim of the crowd.

"We're l-l-lost!" Jay wailed loudly.

Lynn and Norman cried, too. And although Debby was frightened, she remembered her promise to Uncle Ross.

"What if we never get found?" Jay cried. "Never, *never,* NEVER!"

"You stop that, Jay!" Debby said sharply. Then she added something Mother sometimes said, "You ought to know better!"

"*What* should I know better?" Jay sobbed.

"You ought to know—" Debby began, then stopped to search her memory. What should they know to keep them from being afraid?

Then her eyes brightened and she smiled. The others grew quiet.

"You ought to know," she told them, "that *God knows where we are,* even if Uncle Ross doesn't. We can't be lost! God knows we're right here!"

She no longer felt afraid. The other children smiled through their tears.

"Then is Uncle Ross lost?" Jay asked.

Debby shook her head. "No. God knows where he is, too."

Just then they heard Uncle Ross's hearty voice, "Here you are! And not scared a bit!"

The children laughed and all talked at once. "Debby told us that God knew where we were all the time!"

"Wise little Debby," Uncle Ross said.

And off they went to see the panda again.

— —AILEENE SARGENT

"I am with thee, and will keep thee in all places" —Genesis 28:15.

66

Timmy's adventure

Timmy's brother Jack was in school. So was Sister Sue. But Timmy knew they would soon come home, because Mother was preparing lunch. She poured three glasses of milk. One for Jack. One for Sue. And one for Timmy. She took the jar of peanut butter from the shelf and then opened the bread box.

"Oh, Timmy," she said, "there isn't enough bread for our lunch. Do you suppose you could go to the store?"

"Yes!" Timmy said eagerly. "I know the way. . . . down to the corner *this* way, then round the corner and—and the store is at the *next* corner."

"That's right." Mother smiled. "You won't have to cross any streets. And I will wait here at the door."

Timmy felt very proud. He walked along swinging his arms. A little laugh bubbled up inside him as he thought about telling Jack and Sue that he had gone to the store all by himself.

At the first corner he turned. Yes, there was Mother standing in the doorway, waving her hand, just as she had promised. Timmy waved, too. Then round the corner he went, singing over and over, "A loaf of bread, a loaf of bread," until he came to the store.

He bought the bread and left the store. He walked and walked. He turned a corner. And he walked some more.

He looked at the houses. They seemed strange and not at all like the houses he had passed on his way to the store. Suddenly he was afraid. *This* wasn't the street where he lived! He stood still. He knew he hadn't crossed any streets. He felt all quivery and oh, so lonely! But he tried not to cry.

Then he remembered something. *"Jesus* is with me," he whispered. It made him feel better, so he said it again, *"Jesus* is with me. . . . with *me."* He drew a big breath and walked back to the corner he had turned. He could see the store down at the other corner. Timmy laughed aloud. *He had turned the wrong way when he came out of the store.*

Timmy skipped along until he came to the right corner and as he turned it he saw Mother still standing in the doorway, waiting for him. Timmy ran the rest of the way home.

What an adventure to tell Jack and Sue as they ate lunch!

How big their eyes grew, as Timmy told how he had lost himself and then found himself, in just a little while.

"Didn't you cry?" Jack asked.

Timmy shook his head. He had saved the best part until last. "I knew Jesus was with me," he said, "and He *always* knows the way. *He* helped me to find the way home. I won't ever be afraid again!"

———AILEENE SARGENT

"I am with thee, and will keep thee in all places" —Genesis 28:15.

67

What Jean found

"It's snowing again," Jean said.

Danny ran to the window. Large soft flakes were drifting down. He was excited. Father was at home today.

"You promised to take us for a snowwalk, Father," he said. "Remember?"

"It does look nice outdoors," Father said. "Get ready and we'll go now."

Mother helped Jean put on her red snowsuit and helped Danny put on his blue one. Father wore his warmest coat.

It was snowing faster now. "I wish we could go to the park," Jean said. "It's so pretty there."

"Then to the park we will go," Father said. "It isn't far."

The park was a wonderland, all glistening white. "Let's make a snowman," Danny said.

So they made a nice round snowball. Then they rolled it and rolled it in the snow until it became almost as tall as Jean and certainly as fat. By the time they had the snowman finished, Jean and Danny were so covered with snow, Father pretended he didn't know which one of them was the real snowman!

It was such fun that they didn't notice how thick and fast the snow was

"I am with thee, and will keep thee in all places" —Genesis 28:15.

falling or how strong the wind was

"Come," Father said. "We must hurry home. This is quite a snowstorm."

Jean held tight to one of Father's hands and Danny was glad to hold the other. They walked as fast as they could, but the snow swirled around them so they could hardly see the path.

"I'm afraid," Jean whimpered. "Maybe we'll *never* get home. And nobody could *ever* find us in all this snow! Just us three, out here alone!"

Tch! Tch! Father teased. "I thought you could count better than that, Jeanie."

Then Danny began to count: "One, two, three. . . . there are *four* of us, Jeanie. *You forgot God.*"

"But—but maybe even God could get lost in a big snowstorm," Jean said.

"O-ho!" Danny laughed. "I guess if God *makes* the snow, He could make it stop if He wanted to."

Jean thought about that. Then she smiled. "I'm not afraid any more," she said. "I guess nothing is too hard for God to do. Is it, Father?"

"No," said Father. "God protects His children always."

The wind stopped blowing so hard. It was easier to walk. Then, almost as suddenly as the snowstorm had started, it was over. Danny's eyes grew big.

"We're home!" he shouted.

Mother opened the door and said, "I wondered if you would be able to find your way home in all that snow."

Jean smiled at Danny and Father. "You needn't have worried, Mother," she said. "God was taking care of us."

— —Aileene Sargent

The two Ellens

The birthday party was over. Ellen had blown out the candles. All the ice cream had been eaten. And now the children were getting ready to go home.

"Mother, can't they stay just a little while longer?" Ellen begged.

"You have played together all afternoon," Mother said.

Ellen began to pout. "Then I'm going home with Janet and Billy."

"No," said Mother. "Darkness falls quickly in winter. It's time for all children, like good little lambs, to be in their own homes."

Mother fastened the last button on the last coat and hurried to the kitchen.

"Say good-by to your friends, Ellen," she called. "And close the door."

But as soon as Mother was out of sight, Ellen quickly put on her coat and ran out after Janet and Billy. The children talked of the fun they had had at the party. Soon they reached John's house. His mother opened the door and he went in. Then they came to Ruth's house. The group was getting smaller, but still Ellen went along. Finally, there were only Janet and Billy. Their mother was surprised to see Ellen.

"Does mother know you came home with Janet and Billy?" she asked.

"I am with thee, and will keep thee in all places" —Genesis 28:15.

Ellen nodded, but her cheeks felt hot. "Are you sure?"

"She—she *said* I could," Ellen answered in a strange voice that didn't sound at all like her own.

She played with Janet and Billy for a while. Then she went to the window and looked out. It was getting dark.

"I have to go home," she said, suddenly. And hurriedly putting on her coat she rushed out the door.

She ran a whole block. Then she slowed down. Finally, her feet began to drag. What would Mother say? *What would Mother think?*

The trees made huge shadows and Ellen felt lonely and sad. What if she didn't have a nice warm home and a good kind mother and father? Tears filled her eyes and ran down her cheeks.

Then out of the shadows she heard a voice. "Ellen? Is that you?"

"Oh, Mother! Mother!" Ellen cried, running into Mother's arms. "It was wrong for me to go and I'm so sorry!"

Mother dried Ellen's tears. "Come," she said gently. "We'll go home now."

"But you don't know the worst part," Ellen said. "There seems to be *two* of me, Mother—a good Me and a bad Me. And the *bad* Me told a lie."

"I see," Mother said. "And is the *good* You going to try harder to do what is right?"

"Oh, yes!" Ellen promised. Then an awful thought came and she whispered, "Does God still love me?"

"Yes, I'm sure He does," Mother said. *"He knows* you are truly sorry for doing wrong."

— —Aileene Sargent

Blow wind, blow!

It was a very cold winter. In the town the houses huddled close together. But out in the country, where Randy lived with his parents, they were a *giant's stride* from one another.

O-o-o-O! roared the north wind at the windows and doors.

E-e-e-E! shrieked the west wind down the chimney.

" 'Twill blow the house down!" Randy's father exclaimed.

"Hush," warned his wife. "You will frighten the child."

But Randy laughed. "I'm not afraid," he said. "Because *God* holds the winds in His hand."

"Why, of course!" said Father.

A little later Father had to go out to the barn to feed the animals.

"I want to go, too," Randy said.

"No, no," Mother said. "It is too cold for a child to go out today."

"But God wouldn't let the cold wind blow if we didn't have clothes to keep us warm," Randy reminded her. "See! My coat is thick as the wool on the lambs."

"So it is," Mother agreed, and helped to bundle him into his warm coat.

"I am with thee, and will keep thee in all places" —Genesis 28:15.

Randy's cheeks and nose were nipped pink when Randy and Father returned, and the house seemed cozy and warm. But Father had to feed the fires so much wood, he began to worry again.

"We will not have enough wood to last through the winter," he complained.

This time Randy didn't say anything. He did not know how God could send them more wood for their fires.

One day Father trudged through the snow to visit their neighbor. When he came home he said, "They have very little food and cannot get to town to buy more until the storm passes."

"Then," said Mother, "take them some of ours, for we have plenty."

While they were heaping baskets with food, they heard a shout. "Neighbor! I have brought you some wood!" And there was the neighbor with his wagon half full of wood. Randy's father ran out to help unload it, then brought the neighbor into the house to get warm.

"Take these baskets home in your empty wagon," Mother said. "You had more wood than you needed. We have more food than we need. So we shall share."

Randy clapped his hands happily. "See!" he cried. "God gives us all we need, if we just share our *too-much* with those who do not have enough."

And with this they all agreed.

O-o-o-O! moaned the north wind at every crack and cranny.

E-e-e-E! wailed the west wind.

But Randy and his father and mother did not mind at all, for they all knew about God's wonderful care.

— —Aileene Sargent

70

The sled

Snow lay like a soft blanket on the ground. The houses looked like enormous cakes, topped with fluffy white frosting. Children played with sleds. Everyone had a sled except Bobby and his brothers, Dick and Bruce.

"We can make a snow fort," said Dick.

"Sure," said Bruce.

By the time Bobby got into his snowsuit, Dick and Bruce were nowhere in sight. Bobby looked everywhere. At last he found them, *behind* the church at the corner. And they had a sled!

"Where did you get it?" Bobby asked.

"It's brand-new!" Bruce said.

"And it's *ours!*" added Dick.

Bobby could see that it was brand-new. But he had seen it before.

"That's Kenny's sled," he told them.

"We *found* it," Bruce said. "So it's *ours.* Isn't it, Dick?"

"Sure is!" Dick picked up the pull-rope. "Come on. I'll give you a ride."

Bobby and Bruce sat on the sled. Away they went!

"Whe-e-e!" yelled Bruce.

But somehow it wasn't as much fun as Bobby had expected.

"Now I'll pull," Bruce said.

"I will not forget Thy Word"
—Psalm 119:16.

But Bobby scrambled to his feet. "I'm going home," he said.

When he got home he looked at the colored pictures on his Sunday School storypapers. Here was one about God's Word being given to the people. Bobby wondered what God would want them to do about—*something they had found . . . .*

Suddenly he began to struggle into his snowsuit again. He ran from the house. He ran down the street. He saw Kenny standing in front of his house.

"Did you see my sled?" Kenny asked.

Bobby didn't stop. "You wait right there," he called as he sped past.

He found Dick and Bruce still playing behind the church.

"Get off!" he said. "That's Kenny's sled. And it's *wrong* to take it!"

The boys looked at one another. Both looked ashamed. Then Bruce pulled the sled around to the street. Dick and Bobby followed. Kenny was still there.

"Is this your sled?" Bruce asked.

"Yes!" said Kenny. "That's mine."

"We—borrowed it," Dick said. "But we shouldn't have, without asking."

"Don't you have a sled of your own?" Kenny asked.

The three boys shook their heads.

"Well, I have another one," Kenny said. "You may have it, because I got this new one for Christmas."

So Kenny brought the other sled and gave it to Bobby and Dick and Bruce.

How glad they were that they had given back the sled! For they knew that God was watching them—even when they played behind the church.

— —AILEENE SARGENT

The kind uncle

Nobody had ever written a letter to Carol before. So Grandmother's letter was quite a surprise. The letter read:

Dear Carol,

I should like to have you visit me. Your uncle will come for you next Tuesday.

Lovingly,
Grandmother

Carol loved to visit Grandmother. But one thing troubled her. *Which* uncle was coming for her? The kind one or the cross one? Carol hoped it would be the *kind* one.

Mother packed her clothes in a suitcase and Carol chose one storybook. "I'll take my Bible storybook," she said. "It has all kinds of stories."

When Carol was ready she looked out the window. A man was coming up the walk. It was the *cross* uncle!

Father drove them to the railroad station. Then she was sitting in the train, with Uncle Jack filling up most of the seat beside her. She knew he had important things to think about, so she looked out the window and listened to the *clickity-clack* of the wheels.

She looked at the book's pictures.

"I will not forget Thy Word"
—Psalm 119:16.

Carol grew tired of sitting still. She pressed her hands hard on her knees.

"Getting tired?" asked Uncle Jack.

"My legs want to run," Carol said.

Uncle Jack threw back his head and laughed!

"Why, Uncle Jack!" Carol exclaimed.

Uncle Jack looked surprised himself. "Don't laugh very much, do I?"

"Oh, but you *should,"* Carol said. "There's *so much of you* to laugh!"

That made Uncle Jack laugh harder than ever. So Carol laughed, too.

Then Carol said, "Read me a story, Uncle Jack? *This* one about God's Book that was lost for years and years."

When the story was finished, Carol asked, "Have you a Bible, Uncle Jack?"

"Y-e-e-s," said Uncle Jack, slowly. "But I don't know where it is."

Carol looked at the picture again. "You know something, Uncle Jack? This Bible wasn't *really* lost. The people had just *forgotten* it."

Uncle Jack was very quiet. Then he said, "You know something, Carol? *My* Bible isn't lost either. I have forgotten where I put it. Let's look for it as soon as we get home. Shall we?"

The train stopped with a jerk.

"Here we are," said Uncle Jack.

It was a wonderful visit! Each night Uncle Jack read to Carol in a new gentle voice, from the Bible storybook. Best of all, instead of having a *kind* uncle and a *cross* uncle, Carol discovered that she had *two kind uncles*. And all because Uncle Jack found the Bible he had forgotten.

— —AILEENE SARGENT

Friends of Jesus

Tommy and Paul were quarreling. They had been such good friends, but now they were angry. Tommy took his dump truck and backed away from Paul.

"I won't play with you any more!" he said, stamping his foot.

"I don't care," Paul answered. "I'll play with Jimmy. He's my friend."

Jimmy had been Tommy's friend, too. But if he played with Paul. . . .

Tommy puzzled over this for a moment. Then he decided he would have to be mad at Jimmy, too. So he had lost *two* friends.

"Michael is my friend," Tommy said. "I have lots of friends!"

"Ha!" Paul laughed. "Who are they?"

Tommy's face was red with anger. "My mother is my friend," he cried. "And my father and—and—*Jesus* is my Friend!"

There! Let Paul boast of his friends. Nobody could be a better friend than Jesus.

"How do you know?" Paul asked.

"I just *know!*" Tommy shouted. Then he turned and ran home.

At home he played alone. But he wasn't at all happy. He felt troubled and ashamed.

"The Lord is my Helper"
—Hebrews 13:6.

"It's a lovely day," Mother said. "Why don't you play outdoors?"

Tommy shook his head. "I don't want to." Then he asked, "Mother, Jesus *is* my Friend, isn't He?"

"He surely is!" Mother said. "He loves all little children, everywhere."

"Even Paul and Jimmy?"

"Why, of course He loves Paul and Jimmy," Mother said. "What made you think He would not be *their* Friend?"

Tommy felt too mixed up to try to explain it to Mother. He was mad at Paul. Then he felt angry at Jimmy, just because Jimmy kept on being Paul's friend. But he knew that Jesus wouldn't stop loving *them* just because Tommy was no longer their friend. It *was* kind of mixed up. . . .

But, Tommy thought, if you have a friend and you love him, you'd surely want to please him. Would Jesus be pleased when His friends quarreled with one another?

Finally Tommy said, "I guess it would make Jesus very sad if I stop being friends with some of *His* friends. Wouldn't it, Mother?"

"Yes," Mother said. "I think it would make Him very sad."

Tommy got his dump truck and shovel and went down the street to where Paul and Jimmy were playing.

"Please let's be friends again," he said. "Jesus really *is* my Friend, Paul. But he's *your* Friend, too. And if we want to please Him, we've just got to be friends with each other!"

"Sure," said Paul, smiling. "I think He'd want us to be friends."

—AILEENE SARGENT

The big something

Anne's brothers and sisters called her *The Questionbox*, because she asked so many questions.

"Anne doesn't ask silly questions," Father said. "She is learning things."

"If I could put together all the things I learn," Anne said, "wouldn't it make a *big something*, Father?"

"Yes," Father agreed. "It certainly would make a big something!"

So Anne kept on asking questions and trying to remember and save up all the things she learned.

One day Mother was baking a cake. Anne watched her sift flour into a bowl, then she asked: "Where does flour come from, Mother?"

"First the farmer plants some seed in the ground," Mother said. "Then God makes the sun shine and sends the rain. So the seed grows into tall grain. And the grain is sent to a mill where it is ground into flour."

The other children laughed and sang out: "Questionbox, Questionbox, tell us, we say! How many things did you learn today?"

"The Lord is my Helper"
—Hebrews 13:6.

But Anne didn't care if they teased her.

When Mother was making a new dress Anne asked, "Mother, where did the cloth come from?"

And again Mother explained: "Cotton grows from a tiny seed, like many other things. The fluffy balls are picked and sent to a factory to be spun into thread, then woven into cloth."

"Questionbox, Questionbox, tell us, we say! How many things did you learn today?" the children laughed and sang.

But Anne laughed, too.

The next morning when Father said, "Good-by," Anne clung to him.

"Father," she asked, "why can't you stay at home with us, as Mother does?"

"You see, Anne," Father said, "Mother takes care of you at home. But I go to work each day to earn money to buy the things we need."

All that day Anne thought about the many things she had learned. It seemed to her they were all part of a *great big something*. And then, suddenly, she knew! The secret *something* that made all these wonderful things wasn't a *something* at all. It was *Someone*.

That evening when the family sat down around the dinner table, Father bowed his head. Anne spoke quickly: "May I ask the blessing?"

"Of course," Father said.

So Anne bowed her head and prayed:
"Thank You, God, for food to eat.
Thank You for the clothes we wear,
For our home so warm and sweet,
And for our parents' loving care.
Oh, thank You, God, for *everything*."

—Aileene Sargent

Philip and The Finisher

It was very strange to lie in bed in the daytime and watch other people walking about. Philip could hear children outdoors but he didn't even want to play. He knew he must be very sick because Mother looked so worried.

The doctor had come and gone. Father had hurried to the drugstore for medicine. Philip didn't like the medicine but Father explained that the doctor was trying to make him well and Philip had to help. So he bravely swallowed each spoonful.

Then his aunt came to see him. But he felt too tired to talk. And that was strange, too. Because he loved Aunt Mildred and was happy when she came.

Mother laid her hand on his head again. Everybody was so good to him. . . . so kind. . . . so gentle. . . . Maybe it would cheer them up if he talked a little. But what about? He tried hard to think of something nice. And after a few moments he smiled.

"Hi, Aunt Mildred," he said.

"Hi," she said, with a loving smile.

Then he looked at Mother.

"There is nothing too hard for Thee" —Jeremiah 32:17.

"Mother," he said, "remember the rich man's son who was sick?"

"Yes, Philip," Mother answered.

"Wouldn't it be wonderful," Philip went on, "if Jesus were in the next town to ours *now?* Father could go and tell Him about me and maybe He would come and make *me* well."

"He *is* in the next town!" Aunt Mildred said. "And He is *right here in our town, too.*"

Mother nodded. "That's right. Nobody needs to travel about *looking* for Jesus the way they did when He was here on earth. *You* know that, Philip."

"Why, yes!" Philip said. "Just as our song says, 'I cannot see Him smile at me, or feel His hand today; But I can *know* that He is near, *each time I bow to pray.'* "

As Philip closed his eyes to pray, Mother and Aunt Mildred bowed their heads and together they asked Jesus to make Philip well.

Philip didn't know when they stopped praying, because he fell asleep.

When he awakened the lamp was lit and Father had come home from work.

"He's had such a good long sleep," he heard Mother whisper.

And just then the doctor walked into the room. "What's this?" The doctor's voice boomed out in surprise. "I left a sick boy here this morning! Now I come back and find him better!"

Philip looked at the doctor gravely.

"I guess it took three of us," he said. *"You* gave me the medicine. *I* had to take it. But *my Friend, Jesus, had to finish the job.*"

— —Aileene Sargent

75

Little eyes, little ears

As Virginia came out to play she saw her friends, Dale and Marty and Helen, all sitting on their heels, watching something on the sidewalk.

"What have you got?" Virginia asked.

Dale looked up. "It's a bug," he said. "A silly bug. He keeps going back and forth and back and forth."

Virginia stooped down to look. Along a crack in the sidewalk a tiny stream of water trickled.

"He's trying to get across the water," she said. "Can't you see? It must look as big as a river to him."

"Why, yes!" Helen agreed.

"Well, there's a piece of wood lying right across this great big river." Marty laughed. "Can't he see it?"

"Maybe he doesn't know he could get across that way," Virginia said.

The children all talked at once. "Here, Mister Bug! Come on, Mister Bug! Here's a bridge for you over here."

But still the little bug scurried back and forth, back and forth.

"I guess his ears are too little to hear us," Helen said. "Maybe he thinks we're giants."

"There is nothing too hard for Thee" —Jeremiah 32:17.

"Ho! Ho!" Marty roared in a loud voice. He held his thumb over the bug. "Look! I could squash him with one finger."

"Don't!" Virginia pulled his hand away. "Maybe he has some baby bugs at home."

"Yes!" Dale said. "We ought to help him get across."

"How are you going to help such a silly bug?" Marty asked. "His eyes are too small to see the stick-bridge. And his ears are too small to hear us. . . ."

"He doesn't understand our language," Helen said.

"Well, we can't talk *his* language," Marty said.

"Anyway," Dale insisted, *"we're* so much bigger than he is. We can help him."

"You will just have to trust us, little bug," Virginia said. "We're your friends, even if we do seem scary-big."

She found a twig and held it in front of the bug. At first he tried to scurry away from the stick. But she patiently laid it in his path again. Finally the little bug climbed onto the stick. Then Virginia lifted it across the stream.

The children watched the bug hurry away.

Marty looked thoughtful. "Wouldn't it be strange," he asked, "if *we* had a friend so great we couldn't even see him with *our eyes?*"

"We do!" Virginia cried. "We *have* a Friend who helps us to do things we can't do alone!" And when the others looked puzzled, her joyous laugh rang out. *"We have Jesus!"* she told them.

——AILEENE SARGENT

Karen

The crayon broke in Karen's hand. She wished she had some nice fat crayons like the ones they used in kindergarten. They didn't break so easily and they made a big splash of color on paper.

She went out to play and forgot about crayons until next day in kindergarten, when they began to color pictures.

Karen worked happily for a while, choosing first a green crayon, then a yellow, from the box on the table.

She looked at the box of crayons. There were so many, surely no one would miss a few. She glanced around. Nobody was watching her. The other children worked over their pictures. The teacher was across the room.

Karen reached out her hand and took a red crayon. But she didn't put back the blue one she had been using. She slipped it into her pocket. Then she took a brown one and didn't put back the red one. That went into her pocket too. And another one.

Karen had a strange feeling that everyone could see what she had hidden in her pocket. It seemed the longest day she had ever spent in kindergarten.

At home she put the crayons into her own box. She was afraid to use them because someone might see them and know they were not her own. But what good are crayons if you can't use them? Nobody knew she had them. So she took them to a corner of the room where she could work without being seen.

That night Karen didn't want to go to bed. She begged to stay up a while longer. Then she undressed very slowly.

For this was the time of day when Karen always talked with God, thanking Him for all the good things He had given her, asking Him to bless her family and help her to be good. But today she had been naughty. What could she say to Him?

Maybe it would be better if she did not pray at all tonight. She began to climb into bed but Mother reminded her, "Don't forget your prayers, Karen."

Karen knelt down. She closed her eyes tightly. Soon a big tear squeezed out of each eye and rolled down her cheek.

There was no use pretending. She might be able to hide the crayons from everyone else but *God could see them*. She knew she had made Him very sad. And after all He had done for her, too!

She jumped up and ran to the shelf where her crayons lay. She brought the three fat crayons to Mother.

"I must take these back tomorrow," she said. "I took them."

After she had told God how sorry she was and promised never, never to do such a thing again, she said, "Mother, when I'm bad, it makes God sad. But when I'm good, *we're both glad!*"

— AILEENE SARGENT

"The Lord is good to all"
—Psalm 145:9.

77

Lora's friend

It was Saturday but Father had to go to the office for a little while.

"May I go with you?" Lora coaxed.

"Yes," Father said. "But remember! You mustn't touch anything on the desks."

"I won't," Lora promised.

They drove to a big building, rode up in an elevator and walked down a long corridor until they came to Father's office. He left Lora with Miss Rose while he went to talk to the workmen. Lora watched Miss Rose make her fingers fly over the keys of the typewriter. Then a telephone rang in another room and Miss Rose went to answer it. So Lora was left alone.

She played with the typewriter. Soon the inky black ribbon came loose and spilled in a tangle all over the keys! Lora backed away. She had disobeyed!

On Father's desk were some papers covered with the tiny letters the typewriter made. Lora picked out the letters she knew. Then she stared in horror. Her finger had made ugly black smears on the clean white paper!

She ran out of the office and down the long corridor, darted through an open door, and hid behind a desk. Lora knew Jesus *died* to save her from her sins. But *whatever would happen to her if she kept on sinning? What could Jesus do about it now?*

She heard Miss Rose calling her name but she didn't answer. Then Miss Rose saw her. "Come Lora," she said.

"No, no!" Lora sobbed. "I promised not to touch anything but I did. Maybe Father will punish me!"

"Your father loves you," Miss Rose said. "So do I. If I could take the punishment for you, I would."

"But you can't," Lora said sadly.

Yet it was comforting to know that Miss Rose would like to help. Miss Rose was the best friend she had! She held her friend's hand and went back to the office to wait for Father.

When Father returned he looked at the smeared papers and saw Miss Rose fixing her typewriter. Then he looked at Lora's sorry face and held out his arms.

Lora ran to him. "I'm truly sorry, Father," she began. Then she stopped short and her eyes filled with wonder. "Father!" she said. "I understand!"

"What?" Father asked, puzzled.

"Why," Lora explained, "*Jesus came to earth to find the people who had gone away from God!* The way Miss Rose came to find me. *And Jesus took the punishment for all the wrong things people did!* Like Miss Rose wanted to take my punishment. But *Jesus is with God now, so He can ask our heavenly Father to forgive us when we sin!*"

Lora turned to Miss Rose. "I guess you'll have to be my *second* best friend," she said, "because Jesus is the *very best Friend I have.*"

— —AILEENE SARGENT

"The Lord is good to all"
—Psalm 145:9.

78

Follow the leader

Sue and Pat, Joe and Tim and Edie all followed Jim.

"Round the corner, touch the tree, hop on one foot. Follow me!" Jim cried.

What fun it was to play *Follow the leader!* Jim climbed and jumped and crawled and ran. Laughing gaily, the other children did everything Jim did.

When playtime was over Edie said, "Let's play this game tomorrow."

"No," Jim said. "Tomorrow is Sunday. Did you forget? We go to Sunday School."

The other children nodded. "Tomorrow we go to Sunday School."

Yes, Jim was a good leader. And they had happy times together until a new boy came to live in the neighborhood. Tom didn't go to Sunday School. On Sundays he went riding with his parents in their shiny yellow car.

"Wish we could ride in it," Jim said.

"My father will take all of you for a ride some day," Tom promised.

Soon Tom was their leader instead of Jim. If Tom ran across someone's lawn, they followed. If Tom didn't go home when his mother called, neither did they obey promptly.

"All power is given unto Me in heaven and in earth"
—Matthew 28:18.

One Saturday Tom said, "Father will take us for a ride tomorrow morning!"

The children clapped their hands.

"We can't go tomorrow morning," Jim said. "It's Sunday. Did you forget?"

Then they began to quarrel. Joe and Edie said they should go to Sunday School. Pat wanted to go with Tom. Tim didn't know what to do.

"What's wrong?" Sue cried unhappily. "We never used to quarrel."

"I know!" Jim said. "We've been following the wrong leader!"

"Yes," Edie said, nodding hard. "We should follow Jim."

Jim laughed and shook his head. "We should follow *Jesus*," he said.

Tom looked around. "How can we? He isn't here."

"He's in heaven," Jim said. "But He promised that we might follow Him there, if we obey *Him* now."

Tom came close to Jim. "How do you know you would like it there?"

Jim looked around at all his friends. He looked at the trees and the birds and the grass and the blue sky.

"God did such a good job when He made this world for us," he said, "I'm sure His heavenly home must be even more wonderful! I just *know* I'll like it!"

The next morning when the children stepped out of their homes to go to Sunday School, what did they see but a shiny yellow car!

Tom jumped out and called his friends, "Sue, Pat, Joe, Tim! Edie! Come on, Jim! To Sunday School," he cried. "Let's go! Move over, Sue! I want to follow Jesus, too!"

——AILEENE SARGENT

79

In the garden

It was spring, and Mr. Robin Redbreast sang as loudly as he could. It was good to live in the high oak tree. He could see everything in the garden. There was Mr. Bee, drinking from the earliest spring flowers; and Mrs. Ant, scurrying in and out of her hill-house; and dainty little Ladybug. But none of them could fly as high as he.

Mr. Caterpillar had crawled almost as high as the robin's nest last summer. But he had grown tired and, resting on a branch, settled down and spun a cocoon around his body.

Mr. Robin trilled proudly. How glad he was that God had made him a bird! He remembered how he had made fun of the poor caterpillar, because he could not fly but had to crawl on the ground.

"Just wait," the caterpillar had said. "Some day I will turn into a butterfly. Then I shall fly!"

Mr. Robin whistled gaily. The idea of that ugly caterpillar turning into a butterfly was ridiculous. There he was, still asleep in his cocoon.

"Come," said the robin to the bee. "I know you can fly. But you cannot fly as high as my nest. Now, can you?"

"I must suck the nectar from these flowers and carry it to our hive," said the bee. "Then we shall make honey. Children love honey."

Mr. Robin hopped over to the anthill. "You cannot fly at all," he said to the ant.

"I am too busy to fly," replied the ant. "I carry food to our queen."

Then the robin called to the ladybug, "Ladybug! Can you fly as high as my nest?"

"I must fly home," said the ladybug. "My children are waiting for me."

Mr. Robin soared in the air again, feeling that he was the most lucky one in all the garden.

The cocoon looked strange today. Why, it was opening! Well! So Mr. Caterpillar was coming out to crawl on the ground again. Mr. Robin would be there to see him and laugh. So he watched and waited.

Finally, a damp-looking creature wriggled out of the cocoon, spread its wings, and hovered in the air.

Mr. Robin stared. This was not the caterpillar who went to sleep in the cocoon! *The caterpillar had turned into a beautiful butterfly.*

Suddenly Mr. Robin felt very humble. He looked at the ant and the bee and the ladybug. Each had some work to do that nobody else could do so well. And God had made them all.

Mr. Robin's throat swelled with song. But now his song was not loud and proud. It was sweet and joyous. He was glad, glad, glad—for the earth and the sky and all living things. And especially for the little blue eggs in his nest.

— —AILEENE SARGENT

"With my song will I praise Him"
—Psalm 28:7.

The lily

Weeks before Easter Grandmother gave Phyllis and June a lily bulb. "Plant it in some earth," she said. At Easter time you will have a beautiful lily."

Phyllis looked at the hard brown bulb and wondered how a flower could come out of such an ugly thing. But they buried the bulb in a pot of earth.

"Now we can't even see it!" Phyllis said. "How silly!" Then she ran off to play and forgot all about the bulb.

But June watered it faithfully. Soon green shoots pushed out of the earth, stems grew taller, leaves appeared. But before the creamy flower bud swelled, Grandmother became sick and died.

The children felt sad, for they had loved her very much. But after a while the sadness was put away inside them and they made plans for a happy Easter.

"What do you like best about Easter?" Phyllis asked. "Candy eggs?"

"I like going to church on Easter," June said.

"I don't remember anything special about that," Phyllis said, frowning.

"The music is special," June said. "But the Easter story is the best part."

"Tell me!" Phyllis begged.

"He is not here, but is risen"
—Luke 24:6.

But June shook her head. "You wait!" she said. "It's the best story of all!"

At last Easter Sunday arrived. The church was beautiful and the music lovely. But when Sunday School was over Phyllis met June with a sulky face.

"It was just a *make-believe* story," she grumbled.

"Oh, no!" June insisted. "It's *true*. Some wicked men killed Jesus . . . ."

"And they nailed Him to a cross," June went on.

Phyllis nodded.

"But afterward," June said, "Jesus came out of the tomb where they buried Him and—*He is alive now!*"

Phyllis shook her head. "Grandmother died," she said, "and we never saw her again."

"But we *will* someday," June insisted.

When they reached home June went to water the lily. *The bud had burst into bloom!*

"Phyllis!" she cried. "Come and see!"

Phyllis came running to look at the pure white blossom with a golden heart.

"On the first Easter Day," June said softly, "our Lord came out of the tomb."

"Like the way the lily broke out of the bulb?" Phyllis asked, wondering.

"Yes," June said. "Our bodies, too, will die. Then we will be given more beautiful bodies than before and rise to live with Him in heaven."

"Then it *wasn't* a make-believe story," Phyllis cried. "And Grandmother will live again, too, when she gets her new body! Oh, I want to sing and sing! *That's* what makes Easter so glad!"

— —Aileene Sargent

Happy day

Mark knew it was Sunday as soon as he awakened that morning. The house was very quiet. It was always that way on Sundays. For that was the day Father and Mother slept late in the morning. Then they would linger over breakfast to decide how to spend the rest of the day. Mother would want Father to fix things around the house. Father would want to wash the car.

Mark didn't like Sundays at all. On all the other days of the week people did the things that seemed to belong to each day. But Sunday was just the empty day of the week.

Mark slipped out of bed and dressed as quietly as he could. He would go and play with his new friend, Jamie. Closing the door softly behind him, he walked down the street to Jamie's house.

"Jamie!" he called, then clapped his hand over his mouth. Maybe Jamie's parents slept late on Sundays, too!

But Jamie opened the door, smiling. "Why are you all dressed up?" Mark asked, following Jamie into the house.

" 'Cause it's Sunday," Jamie told him.

Then Mark saw that Jamie's sister was dressed up, too. And so were his father and mother. Their home was clean and bright and there was a pleasant sound of happy voices. Nobody hushed the children and nobody fussed about work to be done.

"Are Sundays always like this in your house?" Mark asked, wondering.

"Of course," Jamie said. "The first day of the week is the *Lord's* Day. We're going to Sunday School."

"I thought Sunday was the *last* day of the week," Mark said. "That's the way it seems at my house."

"Come to Sunday School with us," Jamie coaxed. "You'll see—it's *first.*"

Mark looked at his play clothes.

"There's plenty of time," Jamie's mother said. "Run, ask your mother if you may go. She'll get you ready."

Mark scampered home again. He opened the door gently and was surprised to see his parents already dressed.

"Where have you been, Mark?" his mother asked. "Come. Eat your breakfast. We're going to Uncle Bert's."

"I don't want to go to Uncle Bert's," Mark said. "Please, Mother. May I go to Sunday School with Jamie?"

Father and Mother were silent.

"Jamie said today is the Lord's Day." Mark looked from one to the other.

"Yes," Father said. "It is. And we should rejoice and be glad in it."

Mother nodded. "If we hurry," she said, "we can all go to Sunday School."

And so Sunday became the brightest and happiest day of the week in Mark's home. For after that Mark's family always spent part of it in the Lord's house and tried to keep the rest of it so the Lord would like to be in *their* house.

— —Aileene Sargent

"Show me Thy ways, O Lord"
—Psalm 25:4.

Handy Andy

Andy watched Mother's hands getting him ready for kindergarten . . . *pull on the sox—and fasten the shoes, put on a cap—and—button the coat.*

"All aboard!" Father called. "The family train is ready to start. Where is that little caboose?"

Andy laughed when they called him "the little caboose." He knew it was because he always trailed along *behind* Sally and Jon. Andy was the last to finish eating at mealtime, the last to come when Mother called. Sally and Jon usually had things done before Andy was ready to begin.

Then Mother got sick. Father had to cook! Sally washed dishes. Jon ran the vacuum cleaner. But Andy, the little caboose, didn't do anything to help. And this made the others cross.

"You're big enough to dress yourself!" Jon said, as he put on Andy's shoes.

"Eat your breakfast!" Sally scolded, as she washed the dishes.

Andy started up the stairs to tell Mother how things were. Then he remembered Mother was sick, so he sat on the stairs to think. What should he do?

"Show me *Thy* ways, O Lord," he whispered. And he waited awhile.

Finally, he went to his room to play with his train. He hitched three cars behind the engine and the little red caboose at the end.

"Clickity-clackety," the wheels said. "Clickity-*clack*—" the cars went off the track! Andy put them back and started the train again. "Clickity-clackety—" and over the cars tumbled!

Andy hitched one car to the engine. It raced merrily round the track. He hitched another car behind the first car. The engine and two cars stayed on the track. The engine and three cars stayed on the track. But when he attached the caboose, the train wouldn't stay on the track. The *littlest* one was slowing up the whole train! Then Andy discovered that the wheels on the caboose just wouldn't go around.

Andy thought, "Maybe the *family train* would run if a little caboose named *Andy* would do his share."

"Thank You, God, for showing me," he whispered. Then he went to the kitchen.

"I'm just the caboose on the family train," he said. "But my wheels work fine. And I want to help."

He took a glass of water to Mother. He helped Sally set the table. He put away his toys. He went to the store.

Next morning Mother was better. How surprised she was to find Andy dressing himself and singing, "*Pull on the sox—and—fasten the shoes, put on a cap—and—button the coat.*"

Soon Andy became so helpful that his family stopped calling him "the little caboose." They called him "Handy Andy," which was much nicer.

— —Aileene Sargent

"Show me Thy ways, O Lord"
—Psalm 25:4.

83

The story lady

Ting - ling - a - ling! The telephone rang and Mother went to answer it.

When she came back she told the family, "My old friend, Betsy Blue, has come to town. How nice it will be to see her again!"

"Is she coming *here,* to *our house?*" Barbara asked in alarm.

"She is at the hotel," Mother said. "But I asked her to stay here with us."

"Of course," Father and Janie said.

"She can't come until dinnertime," Mother went on, "but that will give us time to get ready for her."

Father went to work. Mother and Janie began to clean the guest room. Barbara sulked. She said she didn't like guests!

"I want to go to the playground," she said.

"Let her go, Mother," Janie said. "She won't do anything to help us."

So Barbara went to the playground. A Story Lady had come to tell stories to the children and teach them new games. Excitedly they gathered round to listen.

But somehow, as the story went on and the faces of the other children grew brighter, Barbara felt sad. When the children begged for another story, Barbara was silent.

"Let us love one another"
—1 John 4:7.

"Wouldn't *you* like to hear another story?" the Story Lady asked Barbara.

"It's hard to like what's *coming,*" Barbara said, slowly, "when you feel bad about what happened *before.* I should have helped Mother and Janie."

The Story Lady nodded. "Of course you love Mother and Janie?"

"Oh, yes. It's easy to love people you know." Barbara sighed. "It's just kind of hard to love people you *don't* know. But I think God wants us to. Don't you?"

"I'm sure He does," said the lady.

"Then I must go home," Barbara said.

She ran all the way home. But the guest room was ready and there was nothing for Barbara to do. She hadn't done *anything* to prepare for the guest.

A little later she came into the kitchen holding a big bunch of violets.

"They're for our guest," she said.

"How pretty they are!" Mother replied. "I'm sure she will enjoy them."

They put the violets in a green bowl. Barbara carried them to the guest room.

Just before dinner the doorbell rang.

"Why, it's the Story Lady!" Barbara cried, when Mother opened the door.

Sure enough! Mother's friend was the Story Lady. How glad Barbara was that she had decided to welcome their guest, instead of sulking.

Next morning Barbara walked with Father to the corner.

"I like to have guests," she said.

"Even strangers?" Father asked.

Barbara gave a happy skip. "Yes! You can never tell! This *stranger* turned out to be the Story Lady."

— —AILEENE SARGENT

The echo

Donald went with his father to see the new warehouse. It was a huge building with a high roof and great stone walls. While Father talked with the workmen, Don walked through a door into an empty room. Then he forgot which door he came through and grew frightened.

"Father!" he called.

Father didn't answer but Don distinctly heard a boy call *"Father!"*

He looked around. Where was this boy? "Where are you?" he called.

"Where are you?" the voice repeated.

"What's your name?" Donald asked.

"What's your name?" asked the voice.

Now Don became angry. He stamped his foot and shouted, "I don't like you!"

"I don't like you!" said the voice.

Then Father came to find Donald.

"Father," Don complained, "there's a boy here who says what I say."

Father listened for a moment. Back came Donald's words, clear as could be!

"It's an echo," Father said. "It's your own voice you hear. Try it again."

Donald was still feeling angry but also a little ashamed. Then he smiled and called, "I like you!"

"I like you!" came the cheerful echo.

Don was delighted. He would tell his friend, George, about the echo.

When he got home he found all his playmates gathered round George's gym set. But they weren't playing. They were quarreling.

"What's the matter?" Don asked.

"Aw," George grumbled. "We were going to play circus. But nobody wants to be a clown or a wild animal. They *all* want to be the acrobat. It's *my* trapeze, so I will be the acrobat!"

"Then we won't play with you!" the other children shouted.

One boy started to go home. A girl began to cry. Some said *very* mean things.

"Wait," Don said. "Let's play echo. I will hide. Then the rest of you say things. Say anything you want to say."

The children closed their eyes while Don hid behind the shrubbery.

"It's a silly game," George grumbled.

"It's a silly game," Don echoed in a grumbling voice.

Some of the children began to laugh.

The make-believe echo laughed, too!

They tried calling cross things and tried saying friendly things. But whatever they said, Don, the echo, repeated. Soon they were all laughing.

Don came out from his hiding place.

George said, "I guess we ought to be careful what kind of echo we make."

"I think God would like us to make *friendly* echoes," Don said, softly.

George's cheeks were red but he smiled and said, "Let's play circus. We'll take turns on the trapeze bar."

And all the children made friendly echoes!

— —AILEENE SARGENT

"Let us love one another"
—1 John 4:7.

Whistling boy

For a long time Jeffrey had been trying to whistle like big brother Dick. One day he puckered his lips the way Dick showed him and held his tongue just so— and he *whistled!*

After that he whistled up and down the street and all around the house.

"What is the name of the song you are whistling?" Mother asked.

Jeffrey stopped whistling to think.

"I don't know," he said. It was a song he knew well. But he couldn't remember the name of it, nor could he remember the words.

"Who took my hammer?" Father called.

Jeffrey stopped thinking about the song and thought about the hammer.

"I had it," he said. "I was going to make something."

"Go look for it!" Father ordered.

"Who took my mixing spoon?" Mother asked, frowning.

Jeffrey sighed. "I did," he admitted.

"Then you must find it," Mother said.

It was a great deal of trouble, Jeffrey thought, to have to remember where you put things.

Dick came tramping down the stairs. "Did you take my pen?" he demanded.

"Uh—yes," Jeffrey remembered. "I was writing with your pen, Dick."

"Well, leave my things alone!" Dick said, scowling. "Where is it?"

Now Jeffrey had to find a hammer and a mixing spoon and a pen. What a bother! Why did everyone get so cross just because he borrowed things?

He found the hammer on the front lawn and the mixing spoon in his sandbox. Dick's pen was among his crayons. He returned them to their owners. Then he began whistling again.

What *was* the name of that song?

Suddenly he remembered. He was about to run and tell Mother, when he remembered something else. "When I take things that don't belong to me and lose them," he said to himself, "that makes people cross. And cross people make *un*happy homes."

After a while, Jeffrey took Dick's baseball. Then he laid it down and went to find Dick. "May I play with your ball?" he asked.

"Sure," Dick said. "But bring it back."

Later, he spilled Father's box of nails but he picked them all up again.

And when he wanted to cut pictures from a magazine, he asked, "Mother, may I cut this?"

"Not that one, Jeffrey," Mother said. "But here is one you may cut."

So Jeffrey cut pictures and whistled.

"What's the name of that song you are whistling?" Father asked.

Jeffrey looked up and smiled. "It's *Happy Home for Jesus,*" he said.

And now Jeffrey knew that *he* was helping to make *his* home a happy one.

— —AILEENE SARGENT

"Show me Thy ways, O Lord"
—Psalm 25:4.

Gordon's answer

One day when Gordon went out to play he found his friend, Bert, riding up and down in a new red truck. Lee and Henry had their tool chests and some boards. Carolyn held her doll.

"Will you let us ride in your truck?" Gordon asked Bert.

"Sure," Bert said. He climbed out and let each one have a turn up and down the block. Everyone was happy until Bert began to boast.

"I'm going to be a truck driver when I grow up," he said.

"We're going to be carpenters. Aren't we, Henry?" Lee said, hammering on his board.

Gordon didn't have any tools or a truck. He tried to think of something fine that he could be when he grew up.

"When I grow up I'm going to build a—a—*church*," he told them.

"A big church?" Carolyn asked.

"A great big one," Gordon said.

Bert stopped the truck. "I'll build the walls," he said, "because I have a truck to haul bricks and stone."

"But—but—" Gordon protested.

Lee interrupted, "I will make the roof, because I have a tool chest."

"If you make the roof, then I'll make the seats," Henry decided.

"And I will play the organ!" Carolyn, who was taking piano lessons, excitedly joined in the plan to build a church.

"But *I* thought of it first!" Gordon cried.

"How can you build a church," Bert asked, "when you don't have a truck?"

"You can't make a roof without tools," Lee said.

"Nor chairs, either," Henry added.

"And you don't know how to play the piano," Carolyn said. "So I guess you can't build a church, 'cause you can't do anything."

It wasn't fair, Gordon thought, not to let him do *anything*.

Then he had an idea.

"I guess you couldn't have a church without a roof," he said.

" 'Course not," Lee said.

"And I guess you'd need walls to hold the roof up," Gordon went on.

Bert frowned. "Sure you need walls."

"But an empty building isn't a church," Gordon said.

"Everybody *knows* you've got to have seats in a church," Henry laughed.

"And people to sit in them!" Gordon cried. "So that's what I am going to do to help build the church! *I'm going to bring the people!"*

They all looked at Gordon admiringly. It certainly wouldn't be a church without people.

"But I don't have to wait till I grow up," he said, happily. "I can begin right now."

And so he did. On the very next Sunday Gordon brought a new boy to Sunday School!

—— AILEENE SARGENT

Lisbeth and Louise

Lisbeth and Louise were twins. They looked alike, they dressed alike, and they liked to do things together. But in one way they were different. Lisbeth was a *thoughtful* girl but Louise thought only of herself. Whenever they received any money, Lisbeth wanted to give some of it to the Lord. But Louise always answered, "Father gives us money to put in the offering every Sunday. That's enough to give."

One day Uncle Rob gave them a crisp new dollar bill.

"Let's save some of it for our church," Lisbeth begged.

"No!" said Louise. "It's to spend."

But they could not agree on *how* to spend it. For Lisbeth was sure they would not enjoy anything they might buy, if they did not share this dollar with the Lord.

They never thought of dividing the money, because, you see, they were twins and liked to do things together.

Then they went to spend a few weeks at Grandfather's farm and took the dollar along. But the farm was so far out in the country, there were no stores where they could spend it.

On Sunday Grandfather took them to the small country church. It looked rather sad and forlorn.

"Oh, the poor little church!" Lisbeth cried. "Its paint is peeling off!"

"Why don't the people take care of it?" Louise asked.

"Because there are only a few people here," Grandfather said, "and there is not enough money to care for it as we should."

Louise stood very still. She thought of their own church and the pretty room where she and Lisbeth met with the other children each Sunday to worship God. What if there were not enough people to keep *it* clean and beautiful? What if all the people kept their money for themselves and *forgot* to take care of God's House?

She tugged at Grandfather's coat.

"Grandfather," she whispered. "If Lisbeth and I give our dollar to this church, would it help?"

"It certainly would!" Grandfather said. "Each church is like a different room in God's house. And every part of God's house ought to be beautiful."

"Let's give it!" Lisbeth agreed quickly. "We can take the money out of our bank to spend."

And, surprisingly, Louise said, "Yes. We can give some of *that* to our own church when we get home."

So the twins, Lisbeth and Louise, looked alike and dressed alike and liked to do things together. But now there was no difference between them. For they were both thoughtful and liked to share, *especially* with their church.

——AILEENE SARGENT

"I was glad when they said unto me, Let us go into the house of the Lord" —Psalm 122:1.

The two wishes

There were two things Mary wished. She wished she could do something special for the Lord, and she wished she could grow flowers like their neighbor's, Mr. Holly. She didn't think she could do either of those things.

But one day Mr. Holly said to Mary and her friends, "I am going to give each of you a package of seeds to plant. I will give a prize to the one who has the best garden."

How excited the children were! They took the seeds Mr. Holly gave them and hurried home. Their fathers spaded up the ground and Mr. Holly showed them how to plant the seeds. Then they waited and waited, watering just a little when the ground was dry.

Finally, little green leaves appeared above the ground. They grew taller as the sunny days passed. Then the buds opened into lovely pink petunias.

Mary was so happy that she forgot all about her other wish, until in Sunday School they were talking about pleasing God by taking care of His house. Suddenly Mary had an idea. "Flowers would make our church room pretty, wouldn't they?" she asked.

"Yes," the teacher said smilingly. When Mary got home she said, "I'm going to make the church more beautiful next Sunday."

"That would be very nice," Mother said. "But what about the garden prize?"

Mary thought about that. She wanted so much to win the prize! But Sunday morning, right after breakfast, she went out and picked every flower blooming in her garden. She and Mother took them to the church early.

Now there was no chance of winning the prize, so Mary didn't look at her garden for several days.

The day Mr. Holly paid a visit to each of the small gardens, all the children followed him. Joey had forgotten to water his, so his flowers had died. But Ted and Suzanne had not cut a single flower. Mary wondered which of them would win the prize.

"Now we must look at Mary's garden," Mr. Holly said.

"There's no use," Mary said, shaking her head. "I picked all my flowers."

Mr. Holly said, "Let's go see."

When they got there, Mary stopped and rubbed her eyes in surprise. She had picked every flower. Yet now her garden had flowers again!

"The prize goes to Mary," said Mr. Holly.

"You see," he explained, "Mary has learned a secret about flowers. *The more you cut and give away, the more you have left.*"

So Mary got both her wishes—she grew lovely flowers like Mr. Holly's, and she did something special for the Lord.

— —Aileene Sargent

"I was glad when they said unto me, Let us go into the house of the Lord" —Psalm 122:1.

89

Edwin's share

Edwin and his friends waited outside the church, for Mr. Dobbs, the caretaker, was going away on a vacation.

"Good-by, Mr. Dobbs!" the children called, when he got into his car.

"Good-by, children," Mr. Dobbs answered. *"Take good care of our church."*

"We will, Mr. Dobbs—We will!" But when the car was out of sight the children looked at one another.

"What can *we* do?" Ralph asked.

"Mr. Dobbs cleans the inside of the church and cuts the grass," Joan said. "But we can't do those things."

"There must be something we can do," Edwin said. "What can we do?"

So they thought and thought.

"I know!" Edwin yelled, jumping up and down. "I will put away the books!"

But the next Sunday, before he had a chance to tell the teacher how he planned to help, Ralph said, "Miss Ruth, I will pick up the books."

Edwin was disappointed. He saw that Joan had brought a lovely plant. When Sunday School was over, Edwin knew what he would do. Each week he would give the plant a drink of water. Just then he saw Howard get a glass of water to pour on the plant.

"I'm going to do this every Sunday," Howard told the teacher.

Again Edwin was disappointed. He saw Ralph put away the books. There was one on a chair that Ralph overlooked. So Edwin picked it up and put it on the shelf. Then he noticed Howard had spilled a little water on the table, near the Bible. So Edwin quickly took out his handkerchief and mopped up the water before it could damage the Bible.

All week Edwin tried to think of something he could do to help take care of God's house. But he couldn't think of a single thing.

Next Sunday Linda brought a new Bible marker. She dropped the paper wrapping on the floor. Edwin carried it to the waste basket. A little later he hurriedly picked up a piece of crayon that Howard nearly stepped on.

When Mr. Dobbs came back he visited the children's room. He admired the plant and Bible marker and praised Ralph for taking care of the books.

Edwin hung his head. He wondered if *God* knew how much he longed to have a share in taking care of the church.

He heard Miss Ruth speak his name. "Edwin," she told Mr. Dobbs, "watches for little things that need to be done, such as putting away a forgotten book, wiping up spilled water, and picking up paper and crayon from the floor."

Edwin looked up with wide eyes. Were those things important? Miss Ruth and Mr. Dobbs were smiling their approval.

"Oh," Edwin cried happily, "I *love* to take care of God's house."

— —Aileene Sargent

"I was glad when they said unto me, Let us go into the house of the Lord" —Psalm 122:1.

90

In the toy shop

The toymaker's shop was a wonderful place. He had dolls of every description, dollhouses with tiny furniture, drums, blocks, trains, and even a toy church with a tall steeple pointing to the sky. The church was quite dusty, because it had been there on the shelf a long time. The children, whose parents bought toys for them, often wanted houses for their dolls but never thought of buying a church for them. So the church was forgotten.

The toymaker had made all these things. But it was the dolls he loved best. In fact, he thought of them as his children and wouldn't have been at all surprised, had he peeked into the shop some night, to find them playing and talking together.

It was his custom, when the workday was done, to pat each doll on the head, then wind up the music box and start it playing before he closed the door and left them alone. He imagined what each one would do after he went to bed!

As soon as the music began, the toy soldier swung his arms smartly and lifted his feet high.

"Follow me!" he commanded. "One must learn how to march!"

"It's more fun to play!" cried the boy and girl dolls at the same time.

The engineer never moved from the cab of his engine. "Who will drive the train if I march or play?" he asked.

"The house must be cleaned!" scolded another, briskly working the broom.

"Dear me!" said a lovely lady doll. "There must be *something* on which we agree." Her voice was soft but all the other dolls stopped to listen. "There are so many things to do," she went on, "that we sometimes forget the most important."

"What is more important than work or play?" they asked.

The lovely lady looked at the church. "It is most important," she said, "*to know God and to do His will.*"

And now the other dolls were quiet, for they knew that the lovely lady doll had spoken the truth.

In the morning the toymaker came into the shop and looked around. All the dolls were standing exactly where he had left them. But who had spilled the building blocks? Was it one of the boys, or was it the cat?

Then he saw the lovely lady with one arm outstretched, as though she were pointing at the church. He hadn't remembered leaving her like that, but how beautiful she looked!

The toymaker smiled and kissed her on the head. Then he carefully dusted the little church and put it in the window. "Yes!" he said. "I shall build another church. It is all very well to build houses to live in. But soldiers, engineers, boys and girls—*everybody* ought to have a *church* home, too."

———Aileene Sargent

"I was glad when they said unto me, Let us go into the house of the Lord" —Psalm 122:1.

The stolen trike

Jimmy w a s tired. He pedaled his new tricycle slowly along the sidewalk. The evening was hot and Jimmy couldn't wait to get into the house for a nice cool drink. He left the tricycle on the sidewalk in front of the porch.

"Did you put your tricycle away?" Father asked Jimmy after supper.

"I will," said Jimmy. But he didn't. After his pajamas were on and the lights were turned off he remembered that he had not obeyed his father. He tried not to think about it as he drifted off to sleep.

The morning was bright and sunny, but still cool enough for Jimmy to have fun riding his tricycle before breakfast. But where was it? Jimmy looked around the porch. He looked behind the house. Then big tears rolled down his cheeks. His trike was gone!

Father and Mother looked too, up and down the busy city street. Even sister Tina toddled around saying, "Bike aw gone!"

As Father took up the telephone to call the police station, Jimmy sobbed, "I know I didn't obey, Father. That was a sin. I'll always try to remember after this. Please ask them to find it."

When Father finished talking on the telephone he gathered his family around him.

"What do you suppose we should do before the policeman gets here?"

"Let's pray," said Jimmy. "Maybe when God sees I'm really sorry for my sin and want to obey next time, He'll help the policeman find my tricycle." They all bowed their heads, even sister Tina.

Jimmy saw the big policeman with his blue suit and bright buttons coming toward the house. Jimmy could scarcely believe his eyes. The policeman was pushing Jimmy's new tricycle beside him.

"When did you find it? Who had it? Where was it?" Jimmy shouted all at once, running to the door.

The policeman tipped back his blue hat with the shiny badge on it and laughed at Jimmy. Then he became serious again.

"I found your tricycle three blocks down the street, young man. And it was pushed into the bushes. Someone must have taken it from the front of your house, pulled it that far, and then decided to leave it."

"I . . . I didn't obey my Father last night and left it outside. I know that was wrong," said Jimmy.

"You are a lucky boy to get such a nice trike back," said the policeman, lifting up Jimmy and setting him on the tricycle. "This is a big city and many people want to steal things."

"Thank you for finding it," smiled Jimmy. "And thank You, God, for hearing my prayer," he added.

— LEONA CHOY

"I will be sorry for my sin"
—Psalm 38:18.

Nancy the nurse

Nancy lazily blinked her eyes as the morning sun came through the window. Then she popped them wide open. Today was the day for the Sunday School picnic! In a minute dress—stockings—shoes were on, with no help from Mother.

When Nancy came downstairs, Mother was already in the kitchen. But she wasn't making sandwiches for a picnic. She was putting white cloths in a pan of ice water.

"What are you doing, Mother? Aren't we supposed to get ready for the picnic? Where is our lunch?"

"I'm afraid there will be no picnic for us today, Nancy," answered her Mother. "Bobby is quite sick today. He was sick all night too." Mother carried the pan with ice water upstairs, with Nancy following close behind.

Nancy's lower lip trembled so much that she couldn't talk. But she wasn't thinking of her brother Bobby. She was thinking of the picnic she would miss. It just isn't fair, she thought. He shouldn't get sick on this important day!

Just then she saw little Bobby lying on his bed, looking so sad, that she almost forgot about the picnic.

"Poor Bobby," she said, putting her hand on his hot forehead. "I'll help take care of you. I'll be your nurse!"

"I know God is pleased, Nancy," Mother said with a smile. "We have to forget about ourselves when someone else needs us."

"Let *me* put the cold cloths on his head," begged Nancy. "Then you can make Daddy's breakfast."

"That will be fine," Mother told her, showing her just how to wring out the cloths so that Bobby's head wouldn't get too wet.

In a few moments Mother came back into Bobby's room with a pair of scissors, a jar of paste, and some white and red paper. Soon she had made a little nurse's cap for Nancy and pasted a red cross on the front of it—just like a real nurse. Nancy felt just like skipping around the room as she thought of how important she was to be helping care for Bobby.

Then Mother went downstairs again to do her other work. Nancy saw that Bobby had fallen asleep. So she very carefully put another cool cloth on his head. And then she said to herself, "I must pray for Bobby."

She knelt down beside his bed, closed her eyes, and prayed, "Thank You, Lord, for letting me help care for Bobby. Please make him well real soon—and help everybody else to have a nice time at the picnic too. I'm glad I'm right here helping. I would rather be here than at the picnic."

— —Leona Choy

"Do that which is right and good" —Deuteronomy 6:18.

93

The spot

How excited Jack was the day the new living room rug arrived! He watched the strong men carry the big roll, wrapped all around with paper, into the house.

"Would you like to help me, Jack?" asked Daddy.

Jack did want to. He helped Daddy straighten the rug so that it would look just right. Then he handed Daddy the tacks to fasten the rug down. Everybody helped put the furniture back and then stood and looked. How nice the room looked!

"We must be careful not to spill anything on the rug," said Mother. "We want to keep it nice."

"Yes, we really do," said everybody.

"I'm going to the store," Mother told Jack. "Play outside the house until I come back."

Outside Jack found Charlie, his friend, with his bubble pipe, his bowl of water, and his bubble soap. He was making beautiful bubbles that floated way up into the air, full of lovely colors.

Just then the sun went under the clouds. A few drops of rain fell.

"Let's go into the house and blow bubbles," shouted Jack excitedly.

"Help me, O Lord my God"
—Psalm 109:26.

So they went into Jack's living room and sat down on the floor near the window and blew more pretty bubbles. Charlie blew a big one, almost bigger than an egg.

"Now it's my turn," said Jack. He started to grab the pipe from Charlie.

All at once, over went the bowl of water on the lovely new rug!

Charlie's eyes got very wide. He grabbed his bubble pipe and bowl and ran out the door. "I have to go home," Charlie shouted as he ran off.

Mother was coming up the walk. For a minute Jack didn't know what to do. He wanted to hide or pretend he didn't know about the spot on the rug. Maybe Mother wouldn't see it.

"But Jesus sees it," said Jack to himself. And then he thought of the verse he had learned in Sunday School, "Help me, O Lord my God." He went out to meet Mother.

Quickly he told her everything. Mother set her groceries down as fast as she could. She got two sponges from the kitchen. Both of them got down on their knees to soak up the water into the sponges. They worked hard.

"I'm sorry, Mother," said Jack in a little voice.

"I am happy because you do not hide things from me," she replied. "I'm sure God is pleased too when we tell Him right away when we do wrong. He is always ready to forgive us if we are sorry."

When they got up and looked at the place where the big water spot had been on the new rug, it was all gone!

"God did help me!" said Jack.

— —Leona Choy

The four pennies

"But why can't you go to the store?" asked Judy. "My Mother lets me go."

"Mother says I have to wait until I'm older before I cross the street by myself," said Lily slowly.

"But you won't be by yourself," insisted Judy. "You will be with me."

"I'll go ask Mother," said Lily.

"And ask her for some pennies too."

Lily looked and looked for Mother. Then she remembered. Mother was next door. Just then Lily saw some dimes, nickels, and pennies on the piano bench.

"I wonder what these are for," said Lily. "Maybe I could just take the four pennies. There is so much other money here, it won't be missed."

She took the four pennies and ran out the door to Judy who was waiting.

Lily did not tell Judy that she had not asked Mother. Lily did not tell Judy where she got the four pennies.

When they came to the street, Judy took Lily's hand carefully and then they both crossed the street.

In the drugstore were all kinds of wonderful things to buy. It was hard for Lily to make up her mind. Then she decided on bubble gum and pep-permint patties. But somehow she did not feel very happy on the way home.

"I'll have to go in now," said Judy. "It is nearly time for supper."

Mother had returned and was hurrying to get supper. "Please help me set the table, Lily," she asked. Without saying a word, Lily helped Mother.

At supper Lily kept thinking about the wrong she had done. In the middle of the meal the doorbell rang. The newsboy was collecting money for the newspaper delivery.

"Where is the rest of the money I put on the piano bench?" asked Mother. "Four pennies are missing."

Lily acted as if she were going to cry. Mother got four more pennies from her purse, paid the boy, and came back into the kitchen.

"Mother, I'm sorry," said Lily. "I took the money to spend at the drugstore. And I went to the store with Judy without telling you."

"That is very serious," said Daddy.

"I'm really sorry," said Lily again. "I'll never never do it again. Do you suppose God will forgive me?"

"Lily, God always forgives us when we are truly sorry. We forgive you too," said Mother gently. "If you mean never to do it again, perhaps we can find a way for you to earn those four pennies and pay the money back."

"Oh yes, yes!" said Lily, smiling again. "I want to do that." She felt as if a big load were lifted from her heart. How unhappy she had been when she was doing wrong, and how happy she felt to be forgiven!

— —LEONA CHOY

"Help me, O Lord my God"
—Psalm 109:26.

Moving day

Rudy didn't know whether he was going to be happy or sad. He was moving from his big house to a smaller house in another city nearby. When Mother packed his clothes and toys in a big trunk and talked about the new house, he was happy. When he went outdoors to say good-by to his friends, Jerry and Millie, he was sad.

"Now we won't have anybody to walk to Sunday School with," said Jerry.

"Do you suppose there will be a church in the city where you are moving?" asked Millie.

"Sure," said Rudy. "Nearly everybody loves Jesus and goes to church, I guess."

"No, they don't," said Jerry. "My Daddy told me that lots of people don't even want to go to church."

"Well, I'll bet where we are going everyone loves Jesus. So I think the whole place will be full of nice churches," insisted Rudy.

When the big moving van came to Rudy's house, he jumped with excitement. He watched the moving men load all their things.

The next day when Rudy drove with his family to his new house, he was sure he was going to be happy. Two children stood on Rudy's lawn and watched the moving van unload. Their names were Bill and Ann and they had a dog named Shep.

Rudy said to himself. "Maybe I can go to church with these children."

"Where's your church?" he asked.

"What church?" replied Bill.

"Why the church where you go to Sunday School," said Rudy in surprise.

"We don't go to any school on Sunday," added Ann. "We go swimming and to the movies."

"Let's play with my dog," said Bill. "You want to see him chase a stick and bring it back?" They all played with Shep until time for dinner.

"Ding-ding," went Rudy's new doorbell after they had finished eating. There stood Bill, his new friend, with Shep.

"My Mother says to ask you if you want to go on a picnic with us tomorrow. We're swimming too. Ask your parents," said Bill.

"Oh, thanks!" said Rudy. Then he added slowly, "But we always go to church on Sunday. I'm sorry, but I can't go with you." Again Rudy didn't know whether to feel happy or sad. He was happy because he knew he was pleasing Jesus, but he wanted very much to go on a picnic.

"Well, all right," said Bill. "We're going next Saturday too. Do you think you can go with us then?"

"I'll bet I can!" exclaimed Rudy. "Come on in while I ask." And even Shep was sure of the answer. He thumped his tail happily on the floor.

— —Leona Choy

"Do that which is right and good" —Deuteronomy 6:18.

Chuckie learns

"Lights out at eight," said Mother, as she and Daddy got ready to go to a meeting at the church.

Chuckie was making a garage for all of his cars beside the sofa. "All right, Mother," he said. "Zoom! Here comes the delivery truck."

"There is fresh fruit in the refrigerator for a snack before bedtime," Mother told Linda, the girl who had come to stay with Chuckie.

Chuckie always liked to have Linda come to stay with him. She read good stories to him.

"Let's sing tonight," said Chuckie. Linda put down the storybook and they both went to the piano. They sang and played many songs that Chuckie had already learned in Sunday School.

"I'm hungry now," said Chuckie. Just then the telephone rang and Linda went to answer it. Chuckie went into the pantry. There was the cooky jar. He ate four cookies very quickly, and his mouth was still full when he peeked around the door to see if Linda were still talking.

Then he found candies in a box. He ate a whole handful. Mother won't notice that these are gone, he thought. There was a bag of unshelled peanuts.

"God has power to help"
—II Chronicles 25:8.

Chuckie put two handfuls into his jeans' pockets. Then he heard Linda hang up the telephone.

"It's time for bed, Chuckie," called Linda. "Do you want to eat some fruit?"

Linda washed a shining red apple and gave it to him. Chuckie took one slow bite and put the apple down. "I think I'm not hungry," he said.

After the lights were out and Linda was downstairs again, Chuckie crawled out of his bed. He ate a few peanuts. Then his tummy began to feel strange, so he climbed back into his bed and fell asleep.

When Daddy and Mother came home, Chuckie was very very sick. Mother had to change all his bedclothes and his pajamas. Whenever he thought of food he became even sicker.

Mother found the peanut shells. Then she found the cooky jar, still open, and the box nearly empty of candy.

Next morning Chuckie felt better. When Mother brought some orange juice and toast to his upstairs bedroom he asked, "Why did God make me get sick?"

"God takes care of us, Chuckie. But when we disobey and hurt our bodies by the things we eat and drink, that is wrong," said Mother. "And then God has to show us this by letting us get sick."

"From now on I'm going to help God take care of my body." Chuckie took another sip of good cool orange juice.

——LEONA CHOY

The empty bottle

Denny couldn't think of anything to do. Kitty, his little sister, was asleep. Mother was sewing in the back yard. Daddy was still at work.

Denny walked around the house. Then he walked into the house and upstairs. He got a cool drink of water from the faucet in the bathroom. He saw that the door of the medicine cabinet was open.

"It will be fun to look at the pretty bottles," he said aloud. He pulled a chair from the bedroom and climbed up to the cabinet. Denny did not ask God to help him be strong and not touch things which his Mother had warned him about.

He shook the boxes of pills. He opened them and looked at their pretty colors. He took out one pill, put his tongue on it, and made a face. "Oh, this is bitter!" Then he opened a bottle and smelled it. "Just like cherries!" he said. He put his tongue on the top of the bottle. "This is what Mother gives me when I have a cough. It must be good for me."

Denny saw that there was just a little left in the bottle. He took a little sip from the bottle of red good-tasting

"God has power to help"
—II Chronicles 25:8.

stuff. He took a few more bigger sips and it was all gone. It made him feel warm inside. He shut the cabinet and climbed down.

"Where are you, Denny," called Mother. "It is nearly time for supper."

Denny put the empty bottle in the wastebasket and went downstairs. At the supper table Denny started to feel a little dizzy.

"Mother, I think I want to go to sleep," he said slowly.

"Why, Denny, whatever is the matter?" asked Daddy.

"I'm just sleepy," murmured Denny. Just in time Daddy lifted him up and on his shoulder. Denny was asleep. Mother and Daddy looked at each other with worried faces. Daddy carried Denny up to bed.

Then Daddy found the empty bottle of cough medicine. Mother hurried to telephone the doctor. In a short time the doctor was looking at Denny.

"We must thank God that there was not a lot of medicine in the bottle," said the doctor, "or your Denny would be a very very sick boy. I think he will be all right, but call me if he gets worse. Let him sleep now."

Not until the next day, when the sun was already high in the sky, did Denny wake up.

"I guess I should learn to say 'No' to some things," said Denny, "even though my tongue tells me that they taste good."

"Yes indeed," said Mother. "Some things help us. And some things can sometimes hurt us very very much."

——Leona Choy

Strong gentle hands

Jimmy's Daddy had strong hands. With his hands he could break a strong rope. With his hands he could unscrew lids stuck tightly on Mother's jars. With his hands he could just twist an apple into two pieces!

And Jimmy's Daddy's strong hands were gentle. He could pick Jimmy up without hurting Jimmy's arms. He could roll the ball to Jimmy without rolling it too hard. He could pet little kittens and puppies so gently that they were not afraid of him. They liked Jimmy's Daddy.

Jimmy liked to say, "When I grow up I want my hands to be just like Daddy's hands."

Then Daddy would carefully feel Jimmy's hands, touching them here and there, and nod his head and say, "Yes, I think your hands are growing strong. But are they growing strong *gentle*? I think I saw these hands of yours pounding on the table this morning. I think I saw these hands hitting a little girl yesterday."

Jimmy would hang his head. "It is hard to have strong *gentle* hands."

"God has power to help"
—II Chronicles 25:8.

"We will ask God to help you, Jimmy."

One day Daddy came in the door with something cupped in his two strong gentle hands. "This is for Jimmy!"

"What is it, Daddy?"

"Something that must be touched only with gentle hands," said Daddy. He put his hands down low so that Jimmy could see. And there sat a tiny white puppy. It was not just a tiny puppy, but a *very* tiny puppy.

"It is such a tiny puppy that it must be touched only with gentle hands," Daddy said.

Then Jimmy sat down on the floor, and Daddy put the tiny puppy in Jimmy's lap. Jimmy felt so happy that he wanted to pat the puppy hard and harder. He felt so happy that he wanted to hit the puppy and make it move. He felt so happy that he wanted to squeeze the puppy tightly and more tightly.

But, instead, Jimmy asked God to help him to have strong gentle hands. And God did help him.

Then Jimmy stroked the puppy gently, so gently. Jimmy put both his hands so gently around the puppy. Jimmy patted the puppy's little head so gently. The puppy put his tiny little tongue out and licked Jimmy's fingers.

"He's not afraid of me, Daddy!" Jimmy shouted. "He likes me!"

Daddy smiled down at Jimmy in a very pleased way. "He likes you because you have petted him gently. Now I see that my Jimmy's hands are not only growing strong. They are growing *strong gentle*."

——Wanda Schickling

The littlest cousin

There was always the little country church where June heard Bible stories and learned Bible verses and songs. There was always the white farmhouse, and Father and Mother. There was always the red barn full of animals and hay and chickens. But only once in a long while did aunts and uncles and cousins come to visit!

No wonder June felt so excited when a big car came driving into the yard one afternoon, noisily honking! Out of the car spilled Uncle Jack and Aunt Marie and the biggest cousin and the next-to-the-biggest cousin and the middle cousin, the next-to-the-littlest cousin, and the littlest cousin!

"I'll show you our new baby calf!" said June. Away she ran toward the barn with all the cousins following. But the littlest cousin couldn't keep up!

"I'll show you the chickens," said June. And away she ran with all the cousins following. The littlest cousin wasn't high enough to see over and into the calf pen, so she didn't see the calf. And she couldn't keep up! She began to sniff and cry.

"I'll show you the cats up in the hay mow!" said June. She ran to a ladder and climbed up, up, up. The cousins followed up, up, up until they were all standing in the sweet-smelling hay.

Only the littlest cousin was left at the bottom, and she began to howl. At that the cousins stopped looking for cats and came to look down at the littlest cousin.

"She's such a bother!" said the biggest cousin. The next-to-the-biggest cousin said, "She's always causing trouble!" The middle cousin asked, "What can we do?" The next-to-the-littlest cousin said, "She wants to see the animals, too."

Then June thought of a Bible verse: *"Be ye kind one to another."* She asked the cousins, "Why can't we bring a cat for her to see? Why can't we walk so slowly that she can keep up? Why can't we hold her up to see the animals in the pens?"

The cousins all clapped their hands. "That's the way to do it!" And that's the way they did it! When the littlest cousin saw the cat, she stopped howling. When she saw they were going to walk slowly so that she could keep up, she stopped sniffing and crying. When they held her up to see the rabbits, she clapped her hands and shouted happily. Of course, that made all the cousins and June laugh and laugh and laugh.

"Be ye kind one to another," they sang as they walked to the farmhouse to tell Mother and Father and Aunt Marie and Uncle Jack about everything. And they walked so slowly that the littlest cousin could keep up and this made her very happy.

— —WANDA SCHICKLING

"Be ye kind one to another"
—Ephesians 4:32.

How it happened

How did John Henry McNichols begin to think about grandmothers? He was playing in the sandbox with the boy who lives in the blue house next to the house with the red shutters. The boy who lives in the blue house said, "My grandmother makes cookies for me and tells stories from the Bible. And I am kind to her and help her dry the dishes and put them in the cupboard."

John Henry McNichols soon went into his house and asked, "Do I have a grandmother?" He was very sad when his mother answered, "You have one grandmother but she lives far, far away." John Henry McNichols sighed. "I wish I had a grandmother right next door!"

How did John Henry McNichols begin to think of Mrs. J. Johnson? Mrs. J. Johnson came out of her house with the red shutters and began to call, "Kitty, kitty, kitty, kitty." Her hair was gray. Her face was very sweet and she looked like a grandmother.

John Henry McNichols went next door into Mrs. J. Johnson's yard and said, "I'll look for your kitten."

"That would be very kind of you."

Then John Henry McNichols ran everywhere through Mrs. J. Johnson's yard. He looked up in trees. He looked around bushes, into boxes, and behind rocks and flower beds. When he saw the kitten hiding in a tuft of grass, he shouted, "Here she is!" and picked her up gently. Mrs. J. Johnson looked ever so pleased. She started toward her house with the kitten under her arm. John Henry McNichols followed her and asked, "Do you make cookies for your grandchildren and tell them Bible stories?"

Mrs. J. Johnson turned around and just looked at John Henry McNichols as though he had made her think of something very important. "I *would* make cookies for them and tell them stories, but my grandchildren are far, far away."

"My grandmother is far, far away," said John Henry McNichols.

"Then why don't we pretend that I'm your grandmother?" asked Mrs. J. Johnson. "I'll make cookies for you and tell stories from the Bible."

"And I'll be kind and help you to find your kitten when she's lost."

And that is how it happened that John Henry McNichols has a grandmother living right next door!

The very next day John Henry McNichols told the boy who lives in the blue house all about his pretend grandmother and the cookies she would make and the Bible stories she would tell and how John Henry McNichols would be kind to *his* grandmother.

The boy who lives in the blue house asked, "Who *is* your grandmother?"

John Henry McNichols answered proudly, *"It's Mrs. J. Johnson!"*

— —Wanda Schickling

"Be ye kind one to another"
—Ephesians 4:32.

The little house

After breakfast the fathers came out of their houses each day and went to work. The grown-up boys and girls went to work or to high school. The in-between boys and girls went to the brick school just three blocks away. The small children wished they too had somewhere to go.

One morning the small children went together to the Little House to see the kind lady and man who lived there. How disappointed they were to see that the people had moved away! The Little House was empty and bare.

Next morning the small children went again to see the Little House. How happy they were to see that the Little House was full of boxes and beds, tables and chairs. A small girl was helping by taking pots and pans from a box and unwrapping the papers that were around them.

The children crept quietly to the door of the Little House and asked shyly, "Can you come out to play?"

Her mother and father said, "Yes, Margaret may go out to play."

The children felt happy, and they waited while Margaret came from be-

hind the big box and slowly, slowly, slowly walked toward the children. Then they looked at Margaret's legs and understood why she walked slowly, slowly. They saw heavy steel braces that helped her legs stand straight and to walk.

"I can't run," said Margaret.

How sad the children felt! And they wondered how Margaret could play with them if she couldn't run or walk quickly. Then one girl remembered a Bible verse. She said, *"Be kind one to another."*

"Yes!" shouted the children: *"Be ye kind one to another!"* They all felt happy, remembering that verse.

Then one child said, "We can play ball! I'll run after the ball for her."

Another child said, "We can ride our tricycles. Margaret can stand on the back of mine."

A third child said, "We can play house. Margaret can be the mother."

Oh, what fun they had together! Margaret's father and mother kept looking out and smiling at them. The children thought how happy it was to be kind. They had never loved the Little House as much as they did that morning.

And after that, when the fathers and the grown-up boys and girls and the in-between boys and girls came from their houses after breakfast and hurried away, the small children had somewhere to go, too. It was a place where they were always welcome, because of their kindness.

They went to the Little House.

"Be ye kind one to another"
—Ephesians 4:32.

———WANDA SCHICKLING

Steps

When Jerry awoke, Mother asked, "What would you like this morning, Jerry?"

Jerry answered, "I'd like a special breakfast of waffles. And I'd like to be kind because Jesus is kind. And I'd like to go up and down lots of *steps!*"

"Fine," said Mother. "I must return a measuring cup to Mrs. Brown on the second floor. Will you kindly take it?"

So Jerry ate his waffles, washed his hands again, and took the measuring cup.

       step
     step
   step
 step

He reached the second floor, went to Mrs. Brown's door, and pushed the buzzer beside the doorknob. When Mrs. Brown came and saw her measuring cup, she looked very pleased.

"Thank you, Jerry! And what are you doing this morning?"

Jerry felt very happy. "I'm being kind to everyone because Jesus is kind to me, and I'm going up and down *steps!*"

"Steps?" asked Mrs. Brown. "Why, I have a pretty luncheon cloth borrowed from Mrs. Black up on the third floor. Would you kindly return it?"

Jerry took the pretty cloth very carefully in his hands and went to the steps.

       step
     step
   step
 step

He reached the third floor, went to Mrs. Black's door and pushed the buzzer beside the doorknob. When Mrs. Black came and saw her luncheon cloth, she looked very pleased and smiled.

"Thank you, Jerry! What are you doing this morning?"

Jerry felt very happy. "I'm being kind to everyone because Jesus is kind to me. And I'm going up and down the *steps!*"

"Steps?" asked Mrs. Black. "Why, I have a cakepan borrowed from your own mother last week. Could you kindly return it for me?"

Jerry smiled and took the cakepan.

step
   step
      step
        step

Soon he reached the second floor. And
step
    step
      step
        step

He reached the first floor! Then he hurried into his house and shouted, "Here I am, Mother!"

Mother saw her cakepan and looked pleased. She gave Jerry a big hug and asked him if he were happy.

"Yes, I am happy!" answered Jerry. "Because it's nice to be kind to everyone and to go

up$^{pp^{pp^{ppp}}}$ and do$_{wn_{nn_{nn}}}$ STEPS!"

— —WANDA SCHICKLING

"Be ye kind one to another"
—Ephesians 4:32.

103

Big enough

Just before leaving for town, Uncle Jack called the twins. His eyes were twinkling as he leaned down to whisper something. As soon as they had heard, the twins clapped their hands, jumped up and down, and shouted, "Good! Good!"

"What? What? Tell me! Tell me!" begged their younger brother Dean.

The twins stopped jumping and put their mouths close to Dean's ear. They whispered, "Are you big enough to keep a secret?"

"Yes, yes!" said Dean.

"Uncle Jack is going to bring his new red car home this afternoon. He wants to surprise Father and Mother. Don't tell."

"I won't tell," whispered Dean.

Then the twins whispered something to each other and laughed and clapped their hands happily.

"What? What? Tell me! Tell me!"

"Are you big enough to keep another secret, and to be kind and helpful?"

"Yes, yes!" said Dean.

They whispered, "We're going to clean up the garage so Uncle Jack can put his new car into it. He'll be surprised!"

Then all three boys joined hands and laughed and jumped all the way to the garage. They felt happy to have good secrets and to plan a kind surprise for Uncle Jack.

Soon they were busy working. The twins pulled some large boards to the side of the garage and put them in a neat pile. Dean was big enough to help by carrying some small boards and placing them on top of the pile. The twins moved some large boxes to the back of the garage. Dean was big enough to help by putting a hammer, some nails, and some paint cans on the proper shelves. The twins swept the garage floor with the big brushy broom. Dean was big enough to help by emptying the dustpan into the big trash basket beside the garage.

At last the work was finished! When Father and Mother asked them at lunch why they had cleaned the garage, the three boys giggled. Dean wished he could tell, but he was big enough to keep the secrets.

Suddenly they heard a loud horn blow. They all ran outside. There was a beautiful red car with Uncle Jack behind the steering wheel. Father and Mother were so surprised! Then Uncle Jack looked at the garage and *he* was surprised! He thanked the boys.

Then they locked up the house and climbed into the new red car and went for a ride and came back and put the car into the clean garage.

All that time Dean was very happy. He was thinking how nice it was to be big enough to keep secrets, and to be kind and helpful and to have nice surprises.

—— WANDA SCHICKLING

"Be ye kind one to another"
—Ephesians 4:32.